PEARSON EDEXCEL INTERNATIONAL A LEVEL
STATISTICS 3
Student Book

Series Editors: Joe Skrakowski and Harry Smith

Authors: Greg Attwood, Tom Begley, Ian Bettison, Alan Clegg, Martin Crozier, Gill Dyer, Jane Dyer, Keith Gallick, Susan Hooker, Michael Jennings, John Kinoulty, Guilherme Frederico Lima, Jean Littlewood, Bronwen Moran, James Nicholson, Su Nicholson, Laurence Pateman, Keith Pledger, Joe Skrakowski, Harry Smith

Published by Pearson Education Limited, 80 Strand, London, WC2R 0RL.

www.pearsonglobalschools.com

Copies of official specifications for all Pearson qualifications may be found on the website: https://qualifications.pearson.com

Text © Pearson Education Limited 2020
Edited by Eric Pradel
Typeset by Tech-Set Ltd, Gateshead, UK
Original illustrations © Pearson Education Limited 2020
Illustrated by © Tech-Set Ltd, Gateshead, UK
Cover design by © Pearson Education Limited 2020

The rights of Greg Attwood, Tom Begley, Ian Bettison, Alan Clegg, Martin Crozier, Gill Dyer, Jane Dyer, Keith Gallick, Susan Hooker, Michael Jennings, John Kinoulty, Guilherme Frederico Lima, Jean Littlewood, Bronwen Moran, James Nicholson, Su Nicholson, Laurence Pateman, Keith Pledger, Joe Skrakowski and Harry Smith to be identified as the authors of this work have been asserted by them in accordance with the Copyright, Designs and Patents Act 1988.

First published 2020

23 22 21 20
10 9 8 7 6 5 4 3

British Library Cataloguing in Publication Data
A catalogue record for this book is available from the British Library

ISBN 978 1 292245 18 8

Printed in Slovakia by Neografia

Picture Credits
The authors and publisher would like to thank the following individuals and organisations for permission to reproduce photographs:

Shutterstock.com: MPVAN 19, Vit Kovalcik 70, Leigh Prather 88; **Alamy Stock Photo:** Hero Images Inc. 1, PCN Photography 10; **Getty Images:** DuKai photographer 48

Cover images: *Front*: **Getty Images:** Werner Van Steen
Inside front cover: **Shutterstock.com:** Dmitry Lobanov

All other images © Pearson Education Limited 2020
All artwork © Pearson Education Limited 2020

ABOUT THIS BOOK

The following three themes have been fully integrated throughout the Pearson Edexcel International Advanced Level in Mathematics series, so they can be applied alongside your learning.

1. Mathematical argument, language and proof

- Rigorous and consistent approach throughout
- Notation boxes explain key mathematical language and symbols

2. Mathematical problem-solving

- Hundreds of problem-solving questions, fully integrated into the main exercises
- Problem-solving boxes provide tips and strategies
- Challenge questions provide extra stretch

3. Transferable skills

- Transferable skills are embedded throughout this book, in the exercises and in some examples
- These skills are signposted to show students which skills they are using and developing

The Mathematical Problem-Solving Cycle

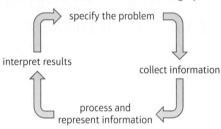

specify the problem → collect information → process and represent information → interpret results

Finding your way around the book

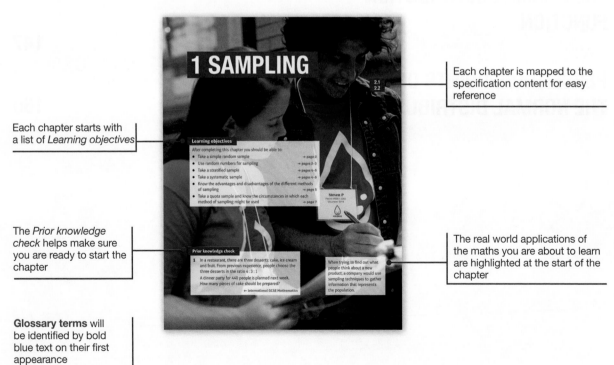

Each chapter is mapped to the specification content for easy reference

Each chapter starts with a list of *Learning objectives*

The *Prior knowledge check* helps make sure you are ready to start the chapter

The real world applications of the maths you are about to learn are highlighted at the start of the chapter

Glossary terms will be identified by bold blue text on their first appearance

Each section begins with an explanation and key learning points

Problem-solving boxes provide hints, tips and strategies, and *Watch out* boxes highlight areas where students often lose marks in their exams

Step-by-step worked examples focus on the key types of questions you'll need to tackle

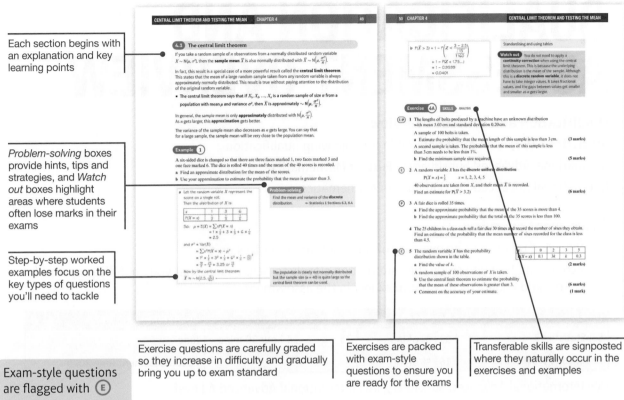

Exercise questions are carefully graded so they increase in difficulty and gradually bring you up to exam standard

Exercises are packed with exam-style questions to ensure you are ready for the exams

Transferable skills are signposted where they naturally occur in the exercises and examples

Exam-style questions are flagged with (E)

Problem-solving questions are flagged with (P)

Each chapter ends with a *Chapter review* and a *Summary of key points*

After every few chapters, a *Review exercise* helps you consolidate your learning with lots of exam-style questions

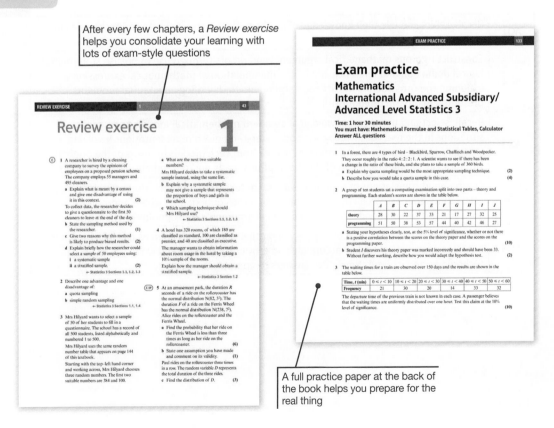

A full practice paper at the back of the book helps you prepare for the real thing

QUALIFICATION AND ASSESSMENT OVERVIEW

Qualification and content overview

Statistics 3 (S3) is an **optional** unit in the following qualifications:

International Advanced Subsidiary in Further Mathematics

International Advanced Level in Further Mathematics

Assessment overview

The following table gives an overview of the assessment for this unit.

We recommend that you study this information closely to help ensure that you are fully prepared for this course and know exactly what to expect in the assessment.

Unit	Percentage	Mark	Time	Availability
S3: Statistics 3	$33\frac{1}{3}$ % of IAS	75	1 hour 30 mins	June
Paper code WST03/01	$16\frac{2}{3}$ % of IAL			First assessment June 2020

IAS: International Advanced Subsidiary, IAL: International Advanced A Level.

Assessment objectives and weightings

		Minimum weighting in IAS and IAL
AO1	Recall, select and use their knowledge of mathematical facts, concepts and techniques in a variety of contexts.	30%
AO2	Construct rigorous mathematical arguments and proofs through use of precise statements, logical deduction and inference and by the manipulation of mathematical expressions, including the construction of extended arguments for handling substantial problems presented in unstructured form.	30%
AO3	Recall, select and use their knowledge of standard mathematical models to represent situations in the real world; recognise and understand given representations involving standard models; present and interpret results from such models in terms of the original situation, including discussion of the assumptions made and refinement of such models.	10%
AO4	Comprehend translations of common realistic contexts into mathematics; use the results of calculations to make predictions, or comment on the context; and, where appropriate, read critically and comprehend longer mathematical arguments or examples of applications.	5%
AO5	Use contemporary calculator technology and other permitted resources (such as formulae booklets or statistical tables) accurately and efficiently; understand when not to use such technology, and its limitations. Give answers to appropriate accuracy.	5%

Relationship of assessment objectives to units

S3	Assessment objective				
	AO1	AO2	AO3	AO4	AO5
Marks out of 75	25–30	20–25	10–15	5–10	5–10
%	$33\frac{1}{3}$–40	$26\frac{2}{3}$–$33\frac{1}{3}$	$13\frac{1}{3}$–20	$6\frac{2}{3}$–$13\frac{1}{3}$	$6\frac{2}{3}$–$13\frac{1}{3}$

Calculators

Students may use a calculator in assessments for these qualifications. Centres are responsible for making sure that calculators used by their students meet the requirements given in the table below.

Students are expected to have available a calculator with at least the following keys: $+$, $-$, $\times$, $\div$, π, x^2, $\sqrt{x}$, $\frac{1}{x}$, x^y, $\ln x$, e^x, $x!$, sine, cosine and tangent and their inverses in degrees and decimals of a degree, and in radians; memory.

Prohibitions

Calculators with any of the following facilities are prohibited in all examinations:

* databanks
* retrieval of text or formulae
* built-in symbolic algebra manipulations
* symbolic differentiation and/or integration
* language translators
* communication with other machines or the internet

Extra online content

Whenever you see an *Online* box, it means that there is extra online content available to support you.

SolutionBank

SolutionBank provides worked solutions for questions in the book.
Download the solutions as a PDF or quickly find the solution you need online.

Use of technology

Explore topics in more detail, visualise problems and consolidate your understanding. Use pre-made GeoGebra activities or Casio resources for a graphic calculator.

Online Find the point of intersection graphically using technology.

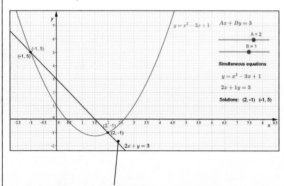

GeoGebra-powered interactives

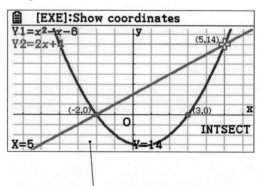

Graphic calculator interactives

Interact with the maths you are learning using GeoGebra's easy-to-use tools

Explore the maths you are learning and gain confidence in using a graphic calculator

Calculator tutorials

Our helpful video tutorials will guide you through how to use your calculator in the exams. They cover both Casio's scientific and colour graphic calculators.

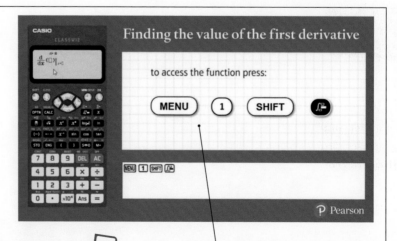

Online Work out each coefficient quickly using the ^nC_r and power functions on your calculator.

Step-by-step guide with audio instructions on exactly which buttons to press and what should appear on your calculator's screen

1 SAMPLING

2.1
2.2

Learning objectives

After completing this chapter you should be able to:

● Take a simple random sample   → page 2
● Use random numbers for sampling   → pages 2–3
● Take a stratified sample   → pages 4–5
● Take a systematic sample   → pages 4–5
● Know the advantages and disadvantages of the different methods
  of sampling   → page 5
● Take a quota sample and know the circumstances in which each
  method of sampling might be used   → page 7

Prior knowledge check

1   In a restaurant, there are three desserts: cake, ice cream
    and fruit. From previous experience, people choose the
    three desserts in the ratio 4 : 3 : 1

    A dinner party for 440 people is planned next week.
    How many pieces of cake should be prepared?

    ← **International GCSE Mathematics**

When trying to find out what
people think about a new
product, a company would use
sampling techniques to gather
information that represents
the population.

1.1 Sampling

In Statistics 2, you learned about populations and **samples**.

Some of the key points about sampling are stated again below:

The size of the sample can affect the validity (i.e. how true something is) of any conclusions drawn.

- The size of the sample depends on the required accuracy and available resources.
- Generally, the larger the sample, the more accurate it is, but it will cost more money or take more time.
- If the population is varied, you need a larger sample than if the population were uniform.
- Different samples can lead to different conclusions due to the natural variation in a population.
- Individual units of a population are known as **sampling units**.
- Often sampling units of a population are individually (separately) named or numbered to form a list called a **sampling frame**.

Example 1

Give a brief explanation, and an example of the use of:

a a **census**   **b** a sample survey

A school wants to carry out a sample survey on their students.

Give an example of:

c a sampling unit   **d** a sampling frame

> **a** Census – every member of the population is observed.
> Example: 10–year national census
> **b** Sample survey – a small population of the population is observed.
> Example: opinion polls
> **c** Sampling unit – the enrolment number of the student.
> **d** Sampling frame – a list of all of the enrolment numbers of the students.

1.2 Using a random number table

Once you have a sampling frame where each sampling unit is a number, you can use a **random number table** (such as the one given in the formula book) to generate random numbers, instead of using a calculator.

The random number table is constructed with great care so that each digit is equally likely to appear.

Suppose you want a sample of 50. You will need to select 50 random numbers from the table. You could start at the top left-hand corner and work down the column. If you reach the bottom of the table, you could start again at the top with the next unused digits along the top row.

However, it is better to start at a randomly-selected place in the table. From there you may travel in any direction. If a number appears that has already appeared, it is ignored (in effect this is sampling without replacement).

Once you have extracted 50 random numbers, the sample is selected from the numbered sampling frame by using these numbers.

In random number sampling, each element is given a number. The numbers of the required elements are selected by using random number tables or other random number generators.

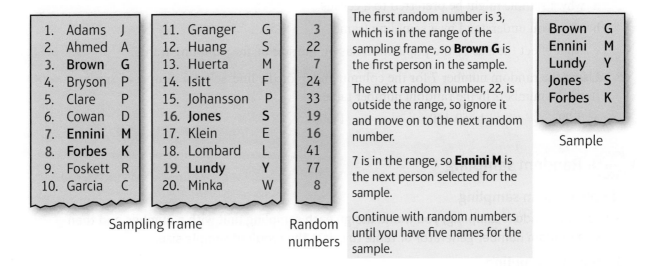

Sampling frame		Random numbers		Sample

1. Adams   J
2. Ahmed   A
3. **Brown**   **G**
4. Bryson   P
5. Clare   P
6. Cowan   D
7. **Ennini**   **M**
8. **Forbes**   **K**
9. Foskett   R
10. Garcia   C

11. Granger   G
12. Huang   S
13. Huerta   M
14. Isitt   F
15. Johansson   P
16. **Jones**   **S**
17. Klein   E
18. Lombard   L
19. **Lundy**   **Y**
20. Minka   W

Random numbers: 3, 22, 7, 24, 33, 19, 16, 41, 77, 8

The first random number is 3, which is in the range of the sampling frame, so **Brown G** is the first person in the sample.

The next random number, 22, is outside the range, so ignore it and move on to the next random number.

7 is in the range, so **Ennini M** is the next person selected for the sample.

Continue with random numbers until you have five names for the sample.

Sample:
Brown   G
Ennini   M
Lundy   Y
Jones   S
Forbes   K

Example 2

You are going to take a sample of size 5 from a population of size 400. Write down the first five random numbers, using the thirteenth column of the table on page 144 and working down.

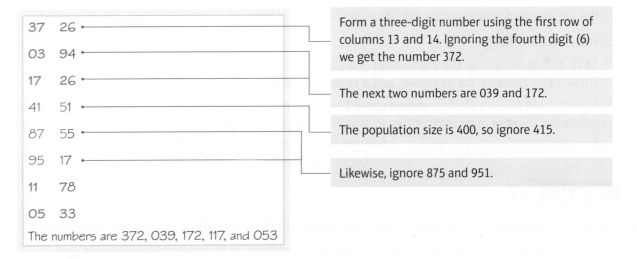

37 26
03 94
17 26
41 51
87 55
95 17
11 78
05 33

The numbers are 372, 039, 172, 117, and 053

Form a three-digit number using the first row of columns 13 and 14. Ignoring the fourth digit (6) we get the number 372.

The next two numbers are 039 and 172.

The population size is 400, so ignore 415.

Likewise, ignore 875 and 951.

Exercise 1A

1   Explain briefly what is meant by the term 'sampling'. Give three advantages of taking a sample instead of a census.

2   Define what is meant by a census. By referring to specific examples, suggest two reasons why a census might be used.

3   A factory makes safety ropes for climbers and has an order to supply 3000 ropes. The buyer wants to know if the load at which the ropes break is more than a certain figure.

   Suggest a reason why a census would not be used for this purpose.

4   Explain:
   a why a sample might be preferred to a census
   b what you understand by a sampling frame
   c what effect the size of the population has on the size of the sampling frame.

5   Using the random number 7 for the column and 3 for the line, select a sample of size 6 from the numbers in the random number table:
   a 0-99   b 50-150   c 1-600

1.3   Random sampling

Simple random sampling

- In simple random sampling, you would assign each sampling unit with a number, and then use a random number generator or table to select the required sample size.

Systematic sampling

- In systematic sampling, the required elements are chosen at regular **intervals** from an ordered list.

For example, if a sample of size 20 was required from a population of 100, you would take every fifth person since $100 \div 20 = 5$.

The first person should be chosen at random. For example, if the first person chosen is number 2 in the list, the remaining sample would be persons 7, 12, 17, etc.

Stratified sampling

- In stratified sampling, the population is divided into mutually exclusive **strata** (males and females, for example) and a random sample is taken from each.

The proportion of each strata sampled should be the same. A simple formula can be used to calculate the number of people we should sample from each stratum:

The number sampled in a stratum = $\dfrac{\text{number in stratum}}{\text{number in population}} \times$ overall sample size

Example 3

A factory manager wants to find out what his workers think about the factory canteen facilities.

The manager gives a questionnaire to a sample of 80 workers. It is thought that different age groups will have different opinions.

There are 75 workers between 18 and 32 years old.

There are 140 workers aged between 33 and 47.

There are 85 workers aged between 48 and 62.

a Write down the name of the method of sampling the manager should use.

b Explain how he could use this method to select a sample of workers' opinions.

---

a Stratified sampling.

b There are: 75 + 140 + 85 = 300 workers altogether.

18–32: $\dfrac{75}{300} \times 80 = 20$ workers

33–47: $\dfrac{140}{300} \times 80 = 37\frac{1}{3} \approx 37$ workers

48–62: $\dfrac{85}{300} \times 80 = 22\frac{2}{3} \approx 23$ workers

Number the workers in each age group. Use a random number table (or generator) to produce the required quantity of random numbers. Give the questionnaire to the workers corresponding to these numbers.

> Find the total number of workers.

> For each age group, find the number of workers needed for the sample.
>
> Where the required number of workers is not a whole number, round to the nearest whole number, making sure that they still add up to 80 workers.

Each method of random sampling has advantages and disadvantages.

Simple random sampling	
Advantages	**Disadvantages**
• Free of **bias** • Easy and inexpensive to implement for small populations and small samples • Each sampling unit has a known and equal chance of selection	• Not suitable when the population size or the sample size is large • A sampling frame is needed

Systematic sampling	
Advantages	**Disadvantages**
• Simple and quick to use • Suitable for large samples and large populations	• A sampling frame is needed • It can introduce bias if the sampling frame is not random

Stratified sampling	
Advantages	**Disadvantages**
• Sample accurately reflects the population structure • Guarantees **proportional** representation of groups within a population	• Population must be clearly **classified** into separate strata • Selection within each stratum suffers from the same disadvantages as simple random sampling

Exercise 1B   **SKILLS**   REASONING/ARGUMENTATION

1 a The head teacher of an infant school wants to take a stratified sample of 20% of the children at the school. The school has the following numbers of children.

Year 1	Year 2	Year 3
40	60	80

Work out how many children in each age group will be in the sample.

b Describe one benefit to the head teacher of using a stratified sample.

> **Problem-solving**
>
> When describing advantages or disadvantages of a particular sampling method, always refer to the context of the question.

2 A survey is carried out on 100 members of the adult population of a small town. The population of the town is 2000. An alphabetical list of the inhabitants of the town is available.

a Explain one limitation of using a systematic sample in this situation.

b Describe a sampling method that would be free of bias for this survey.

3 A gym wants to take a sample of its members. Each member has a 5-digit membership number, and the gym selects every member with a membership number ending 000.

a Is this a systematic sample? Give a reason for your answer.

b Suggest one way of improving the reliability of this sample.

4 A school head teacher wants to get the opinion of year 12 and year 13 students about the facilities available in the common room. The table shows the numbers of students in each year.

	Year 12	Year 13
Male	70	50
Female	85	75

a Suggest a suitable sampling method that might be used to take a sample of 40 students.

b How many students from each gender in each of the two years should the head teacher ask?

5 A factory manager wants to get information about how her employees travel to work. There are 480 employees in the factory, and each has a unique employee number from 1 to 480. Explain how the manager could take a systematic sample of size 30 from these employees.

6 The director of a sports club wants to take a sample of members. Each member has a unique membership number. There are 121 members who play tennis, 145 members who play badminton and 104 members who play squash. No members play more than one sport.

a Explain how the director could take a simple random sample of 30 members and state one disadvantage of this sampling method.

The director decides to take a stratified sample of 30 members.

b State one advantage of this method of sampling.

c Work out the number of members who play each sport that the director should select for the sample.

1.4 Non-random sampling

Quota sampling

- In **quota** sampling, an interviewer or researcher selects a sample that reflects the characteristics of the whole population.

The population is divided into groups according to a given characteristic. The size of each group determines (decides) the proportion of the sample that should have that characteristic.

As an interviewer, you would meet people, assess their group, and then allocate them into the appropriate quota.

This continues until all quotas have been filled. If a person refuses to be interviewed or the quota into which they fit is full, then you simply ignore them and move on to the next person.

Quota sampling	
Advantages	**Disadvantages**
• Allows a small sample to still be representative of the population • No sampling frame required • Quick, easy and inexpensive • Allows for easy comparison between different groups within a population	• Non-random sampling can introduce bias • Population must be divided into groups, which can be costly or inaccurate • Non-responses are not recorded

Exercise 1C    **SKILLS**   ANALYSIS; DECISION MAKING

1 Interviewers at a shopping centre collect information on the spending habits from a total of 40 shoppers. Explain how they could collect the information using quota sampling.

2 Describe the similarities and differences between quota sampling and stratified random sampling.

3 An interviewer stops the first 50 people he sees outside a kebab shop on a Friday evening and asks them about their eating habits.
   a Explain why his sampling method may not be representative.
   b Suggest two improvements he could make to his data collection technique.

4 A researcher is collecting data on the radio listening habits of people in a local town. She asks the first five people she sees entering a supermarket on Monday morning. The number of hours per week each person listens to the radio is given below:

   4   7   6   8   2

   a Use the sample data to work out a prediction for the average number of hours listened per week for the town as a whole.
   b Describe the reliability of the data.
   c Suggest two improvements to the method used.

5 The heights, in metres, of 20 emu are listed below:

1.8	1.9	2.3	1.7	2.1	2.0	2.5	2.7	2.5	2.6
2.3	2.2	2.4	2.3	2.2	2.5	1.9	2.0	2.2	2.5

a Take an opportunity sample of size 5 from the data.

b Starting from the second data value, take a systematic sample of size 5 from the data.

c Calculate the **mean** height for each sample.

d State, with reasons, which sampling method is likely to be more reliable.

> **Hint** An example of an opportunity sample from this data would be to select the first five heights from the list.

Chapter review 1

1 The table shows the daily high temperature (in °C) recorded on the first 15 days of January 2019 in Jacksonville, Florida.

Day of month	1	2	3	4	5	6	7	8	9	10	11	12	13	14	15
Daily high temp (°C)	28	26	27	26	16	21	24	24	18	13	17	22	25	16	13

a Describe how you could use the random number function on your calculator to select a simple random sample of 5 dates from this data.

> **Hint** Make sure you describe your sampling frame.

b Use a simple random sample of 5 dates to estimate the mean high temperature in Jacksonville for the first 15 days of January 2019.

c Use all 15 dates to calculate the mean high temperature in Jacksonville for the first 15 days of January 2019. Comment on the reliability of your two samples.

2 a Give one advantage and one disadvantage of using:
   i a census   **ii** a sample survey.

b It is decided to take a sample of 100 from a population consisting of 500 elements. Explain how you would obtain a simple random sample from this population.

3 a Explain briefly what is meant by:
   i a population   **ii** a sampling frame.

b A market research organisation wants to take a sample of:
   i owners of diesel automobiles in the UK
   ii people living in Oxford who suffered back injuries during July 2017.

   Suggest a suitable sampling frame in each case.

4 Write down one advantage and one disadvantage of using:
   a stratified sampling   **b** simple random sampling.

5 The managing director of a medium-sized airline wants to know what the employees think about the overtime pay scheme. The airline employs 100 pilots and 200 cabin crew.

The managing director decides to ask the pilots.

  a Suggest a reason why this is likely to produce a biased sample.

  b Explain briefly how the managing director could select a sample of 30 employees using:
    i systematic sampling   **ii** stratified sampling   **iii** quota sampling.

6 There are 64 girls and 56 boys in a school.

Explain briefly how you could take a random sample of 15 students using:

  a simple random sampling   **b** stratified sampling.

7 As part of her class project, Deepa decided to estimate the amount of time A level students at her school spent on private study each week. She took a random sample of students from those studying arts subjects, science subjects and a mixture of arts and science subjects. Each student kept a record of the time they spent on private study during the third week of term.

  a Write down the name of the sampling method used by Deepa.

  b Give a reason for using this method and give one advantage this method has over simple random sampling.

Summary of key points

1 • In statistics, a **population** is the whole set of items that are of interest.

  • A **census** observes or measures every member of a population.

2 • A **sample** is a selection of observations taken from a subset of the population which is used to find out information about the population as a whole.

  • Individual units of a population are known as **sampling units**.

  • Often sampling units of a population are individually named or numbered to form a list called a **sampling frame**.

3 • A **simple random sample** of size n is one where every sample of size n has an equal chance of being selected.

  • In **systematic sampling**, the required elements are chosen at regular intervals from an ordered list.

  • In **stratified sampling**, the population is divided into mutually exclusive strata (males and females, for example) and a random sample is taken from each.

  • In **quota sampling**, an interviewer or researcher selects a sample that reflects the characteristics of the whole population.

2 COMBINATIONS OF RANDOM VARIABLES

Learning objectives

After completing this chapter you should be able to:

● Find the distribution of linear combinations and
  functions of normal random variables   → **pages 11-13**
● Solve modelling problems involving combinations
  and functions of normal random variables   → **pages 13-15**

Prior knowledge check

1 A random variable $Y \sim N(20, 4^2)$. Find:
   a $P(Y > 15)$ **b** $P(19 < Y < 22)$
                                     ← **Statistics 1 Section 7.1**

2 Given that $X \sim N(0, 1^2)$, find:
   a p such that $P(X > p) = 0.25$
   b q such that $P(-q < X < q) = 0.7$
                                     ← **Statistics 1 Section 7.3**

3 X is a random variable with $E(X) = 7$ and $Var(X) = 3$.
   Find:
   a $E(2X)$ **b** $Var(3X - 5)$
   c $E(1 - 6X)$ ← **Statistics 1 Section 6.5**

If the times of the first-place
and second-place sprinters are
normally distributed, then the
winning margin will also be
normally distributed.
                          → **Exercise 2A, Q6**

2.1   Combinations of random variables

Two random **variables** are **independent** if the **outcome** of one variable does not affect the **distribution** of the other. You need to be able to combine random variables with different distributions. You will use these two results:

- If X and Y are two independent random variables, then:
  - $E(X + Y) = E(X) + E(Y)$
  - $E(X - Y) = E(X) - E(Y)$

- If X and Y are two independent random variables, then:
  - $\text{Var}(X + Y) = \text{Var}(X) + \text{Var}(Y)$
  - $\text{Var}(X - Y) = \text{Var}(X) + \text{Var}(Y)$

> You do not need to be able to prove these results for your exam.

> **Watch out** You add the **variances** even when you subtract the random variables.

Example 1

If X is a random variable with $E(X) = \mu_1$ and $\text{Var}(X) = \sigma_1^2$, and Y is an independent random variable with $E(Y) = \mu_2$ and $\text{Var}(Y) = \sigma_2^2$, find the mean and variance of:

a $X + Y$ **b** $X - Y$

a $E(X + Y) = E(X) + E(Y)$
$$= \mu_1 + \mu_2$$
$\text{Var}(X + Y) = \text{Var}(X) + \text{Var}(Y)$
$$= \sigma_1^2 + \sigma_2^2$$
b $E(X - Y) = E(X) - E(Y)$
$$= \mu_1 - \mu_2$$
$\text{Var}(X - Y) = \text{Var}(X) + \text{Var}(Y)$
$$= \sigma_1^2 + \sigma_2^2$$

> Variances are always added.

You can combine the above result with standard results about **expectations** and variances of multiples of a random variable to analyse linear combinations of independent random variables.

- If X and Y are two independent random variables, then:
  - $E(aX + bY) = aE(X) + bE(Y)$
  - $E(aX - bY) = aE(X) - bE(Y)$

- If X and Y are two independent random variables, then:
  - $\text{Var}(aX + bY) = a^2\text{Var}(X) + b^2\text{Var}(Y)$
  - $\text{Var}(aX - bY) = a^2\text{Var}(X) + b^2\text{Var}(Y)$

In this chapter you will apply these results to analyse **normally distributed** random variables.

- A linear combination of normally distributed independent random variables is also **normally distributed**.

This result allows you to fully define the distribution of a linear combination of independent normal random variables.

- If X and Y are independent random variables with $X \sim N(\mu_1, \sigma_1^2)$ and $Y \sim N(\mu_2, \sigma_2^2)$, then:
  - $aX + bY \sim N(a\mu_1 + b\mu_2, a^2\sigma_1^2 + b^2\sigma_2^2)$
  - $aX - bY \sim N(a\mu_1 - b\mu_2, a^2\sigma_1^2 + b^2\sigma_2^2)$

You can also use this result to find the distribution of sums of identically distributed independent normal random variables.

- If $X_1, X_2, \ldots, X_n$ are independent identically distributed random variables with

  $X_i \sim N(\mu, \sigma^2)$, then $\sum_{i=1}^{n} X_i \sim N(n\mu, n\sigma^2)$

> **Watch out**   The random variable $\sum_{i=1}^{n} X_i$ is not the same as the random variable nX_1.
>
> For example, $\mathrm{Var}(X_1 + X_2) = \sigma^2 + \sigma^2 = 2\,\mathrm{Var}(X_1)$, but $\mathrm{Var}(2X_1) = 4\,\mathrm{Var}(X_1)$.

Sometimes it is better not to use these formula, and use the expected values and variances as above.

Example (2)   **SKILLS**   PROBLEM-SOLVING

The independent random variables X and Y have distributions $X \sim N(5, 2^2)$ and $Y \sim N(10, 3^2)$.

a Find the distribution of:

   i $A = X + Y$ **ii** $B = 9X - 2Y$

b Find $P(B > 30)$.

The independent random variables Y_1, Y_2, Y_3 and Y_4 all have the same distribution as Y. The random variable Z is defined as:

$$Z = \sum_{i=1}^{4} Y_i$$

c Find the mean and standard deviation of Z.

> **Watch out**   When you subtract random variables you still add the variances.

a i $E(A) = E(X + Y)$

      $= E(X) + E(Y) = 5 + 10 = 15$

   $\mathrm{Var}(A) = \mathrm{Var}(X + Y)$

          $= \mathrm{Var}(X) + \mathrm{Var}(Y) = 4 + 9 = 13$

   $A \sim N(15, 13)$

> There are two distributions which are combined to make A.
>
> $E(A)$ should be written as two expectations combined and $\mathrm{Var}(A)$ should be written as two variances combined.

ii $E(B) = E(9X - 2Y)$

      $= E(9X) - E(2Y)$

      $= 9E(X) - 2E(Y)$

      $= 9 \times 5 - 2 \times 10 = 25$

> There are two distributions which are combined to make B.
>
> $E(B)$ should be written as two expectations combined.

   $\mathrm{Var}(B) = \mathrm{Var}(9X - 2Y)$

         $= \mathrm{Var}(9X) + \mathrm{Var}(2Y)$

         $= 9^2\,\mathrm{Var}(X) + 2^2\,\mathrm{Var}(Y)$

         $= 81 \times 4 + 4 \times 9 = 360$

   $B \sim N(25, 360)$

> $\mathrm{Var}(B)$ should be written as two variances combined.

b $P(B > 30) = 0.3961$

> Be careful with means and standard deviations. The random variable B has variance 360, so it has standard deviation $\sqrt{360}$.

c　$Z = Y_1 + Y_2 + Y_3 + Y_4$

　$E(X) = E(Y_1 + Y_2 + Y_3 + Y_4)$

　　　$= E(Y_1) + E(Y_2) + E(Y_3) + E(Y_4)$

　　　$= 4 \times 10 = 40$

　$Var(Z) = Var(Y_1 + Y_2 + Y_3 + Y_4)$

　　　$= Var(Y_1) + Var(Y_2) + Var(Y_3) + Var(Y_4)$

　　　$= 4 \times 3^2 = 36$

　$Z \sim N(40, 36)$

　So Z has a mean of 40 and a standard deviation of 6.

> There are four distributions which are combined to make Z.
>
> $E(Z)$ should be written as four expectations combined.

> There are four distributions which are combined to make Z.
>
> $Var(Z)$ should be written as four expectations combined.
>
> Splitting the random variable up like this avoids confusing the fact that $Var(4Y)$ and $Var(Y_1 + Y_2 + Y_3 + Y_4)$ are very different.

Example 3　SKILLS　CRITICAL THINKING

The independent random variables X and Y have distributions $X \sim N(25, 6)$ and $Y \sim N(22, 10)$. Find $P(X > Y)$.

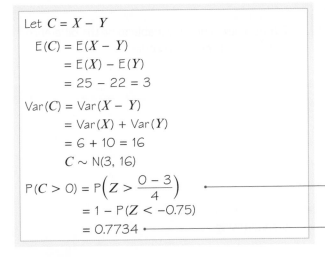

Let $C = X - Y$

　$E(C) = E(X - Y)$

　　　$= E(X) - E(Y)$

　　　$= 25 - 22 = 3$

　$Var(C) = Var(X - Y)$

　　　$= Var(X) + Var(Y)$

　　　$= 6 + 10 = 16$

　　$C \sim N(3, 16)$

$P(C > 0) = P\left(Z > \dfrac{0 - 3}{4}\right)$

　　　$= 1 - P(Z < -0.75)$

　　　$= 0.7734$

Problem-solving

You can compare independent normal random variables by defining a new random variable to be the difference between them. If $X - Y > 0$ then $X > Y$, and if $X - Y < 0$ then $Y > X$.

Standardising

From tables

Example 4　SKILLS　INTERPRETATION; CRITICAL THINKING

Bottles of water are delivered to shops in boxes containing 12 bottles each. The weights of bottles are normally distributed with mean weight 2 kg and standard deviation 0.05 kg. The weights of empty boxes are normally distributed with mean 2.5 kg and standard deviation 0.3 kg.

a Assuming that all random variables are independent, find the **probability** that a full box will weigh between 26 kg and 27 kg.

b Two bottles are selected at random from a box. Find the probability that they differ in weight by more than 0.1 kg.

c Find the weight m that a full box should have on its label so that there is a 1% chance that it weighs more than m.

a Let $W = X_1 + X_2 + \ldots + X_{12} + C$

$E(W) = E(X_1 + X_2 + \ldots + X_{12} + C)$
$\quad\quad = E(X_1) + E(X_2) + \ldots + E(X_{12}) + E(C)$
$\quad\quad = 12 \times 2 + 2.5 = 26.5$

$Var(W) = Var(X_1 + X_2 + \ldots + X_{12} + C)$
$\quad\quad\quad = Var(X_1) + Var(X_2) + \ldots + Var(X_{12})$
$\quad\quad\quad\quad + Var(C)$
$\quad\quad\quad = 12 \times 0.05^2 + 0.3^2 = 0.12$

$W \sim N(26.5, 0.12)$

> There are thirteen distributions here, so split $E(W)$ and $Var(W)$ into thirteen parts.

$P(26 < W < 27)$

> Standardising

$P\left(\dfrac{26 - 26.5}{\sqrt{0.12}} < Z < \dfrac{27 - 26.5}{\sqrt{0.12}}\right)$

$P(-1.44 < Z < 1.44)$

> To use the tables in the formula booklet, keep the z-values to 2 d.p.

$P(Z < 1.44) - P(Z < -1.44)$

$2P(Z < 1.44) - 1 = 2 \times 0.9251 - 1$
$\quad\quad\quad\quad\quad\quad = 0.850 \text{ (3 s.f.)}$

> The value from using the tables is 0.8502

b Let $Y = X_1 - X_2$

$E(Y) = E(X_1 - X_2) = E(X_1) - E(X_2)$
$\quad\quad = 0$

$Var(Y) = Var(X_1 - X_2)$
$\quad\quad\quad = Var(X_1) + Var(X_2)$
$\quad\quad\quad = 0.005$

> Define a new random variable to be the difference in weight between two bottles.

So $Y \sim N(0, 0.005)$

$P(|Y| > 0.1) = 1 - P(-0.1 < Y < 0.1)$
$\quad\quad\quad\quad = 1 - (P(Y < 0.1)$
$\quad\quad\quad\quad\quad - P(Y < -0.1))$
$\quad\quad\quad\quad = 2 - 2P(Y < 0.1)$
$\quad\quad\quad\quad = 2 - 2P\left(Z < \dfrac{0.1 - 0}{\sqrt{0.005}}\right)$

> Standardising

$\quad\quad\quad\quad = 2 - 2P(Z < 1.41)$
$\quad\quad\quad\quad = 2 - 2 \times 0.9207$
$\quad\quad\quad\quad = 0.1586$

c Find m such that $P(W > m) = 0.01$
So $P(W < m) = 0.99$

$P\left(Z < \dfrac{m - 26.5}{\sqrt{0.12}}\right) = 0.99$

$m - \dfrac{26.5}{\sqrt{0.12}} = 2.3263$

> Using the inverse normal table

$m = 2.3263 \times \sqrt{0.12} + 26.5$
$\quad = 27.3 \text{ kg (3 s.f.)}$

Exercise 2A   **SKILLS**   PROBLEM-SOLVING

1 Given the random variables $X \sim N(80, 3^2)$ and $Y \sim N(50, 2^2)$ where X and Y are independent, find the distribution of W where:

a $W = X + Y$ **b** $W = X - Y$

2 Given the random variables $X \sim N(45, 6)$, $Y \sim N(54, 4)$ and $W \sim N(49, 8)$ where X, Y and W are independent, find the distribution of R, where $R = X + Y + W$.

3 X and Y are independent normal random variables. $X \sim N(60, 25)$ and $Y \sim N(50, 16)$. Find the distribution of T where:

a $T = 3X$ **b** $T = 7Y$ **c** $T = 3X + 7Y$ **d** $T = X - 2Y$

4 A, B and C are independent normal random variables. $A \sim N(50, 6)$, $B \sim N(60, 8)$ and $C \sim N(80, 10)$. Find:

a $P(A + B < 115)$ **b** $P(A + B + C > 198)$ **c** $P(B + C < 138)$

d $P(2A + B - C < 70)$ **e** $P(A + 3B - C > 140)$ **f** $P(105 < A + B < 116)$

(P) **5** X and Y are independent random variables with $X \sim N(76, 15)$ and $Y \sim N(80, 10)$. Find:

a $P(Y > X)$ **b** $P(X > Y)$

c the probability that X and Y differ by: **i** less than 3   **ii** more than 7.

(E/P) **6** Two runners recorded the mean and standard deviation of their 100 m sprint times in a table.

	Mean	Standard deviation
Runner A	13.2 seconds	0.9 seconds
Runner B	12.9 seconds	1.3 seconds

a Assuming that each runner's times are normally distributed, find the probability that in a head-to-head race, runner A will win by more than 0.5 seconds.   **(5 marks)**

A 'photo finish' occurs if the winning margin (the difference between two times) is less than 0.1 seconds.

b Find the probability of a 'photo finish'.   **(2 marks)**

(E/P) **7** A factory makes steel rods and steel tubes. The diameter of a steel rod is normally distributed with mean 3.55 cm and standard deviation 0.02 cm. The internal diameter of a steel tube is normally distributed with mean 3.60 cm and standard deviation 0.02 cm.

A rod and a tube are selected at random. Find the probability that the rod cannot pass through the tube.   **(6 marks)**

(E/P) **8** The mass of a randomly selected jar of jam is normally distributed with a mean mass of 1 kg and a standard deviation of 12 g. The jars are packed in boxes of 6 and the mass of the box is normally distributed with mean mass 250 g and standard deviation 10 g. Find the probability that a randomly chosen box of 6 jars will have a mass less than 6.2 kg.   **(6 marks)**

Chapter review (2)

1 X, Y and W are independent normal random variables. $X \sim N(8, 2)$, $Y \sim N(12, 3)$ and $W \sim N(15, 4)$. Find the distribution of A where:

  a $A = X + Y + W$ **b** $A = W - X$ **c** $A = X - Y + 3W$

  d $A = 3X + 4W$ **e** $A = 2X - Y + W$

(E) **2** Given the random variables $X \sim N(20, 5)$ and $Y \sim N(10, 4)$ where X and Y are independent, find:

  a $E(X - Y)$ **(2 marks)**

  b $Var(X - Y)$ **(2 marks)**

  c $P(13 < X - Y < 16)$ **(2 marks)**

(E/P) **3** The random variable R is defined as $R = X + 4Y$, where $X \sim N(8, 2^2)$, $Y \sim N(14, 3^2)$ and X and Y are independent. Find:

  a $E(R)$ **(2 marks)**

  b $Var(R)$ **(2 marks)**

  c $P(R < 41)$ **(2 marks)**

The random variables Y_1, Y_2 and Y_3 are independent and each has the same distribution as Y.

The random variable S is defined as $S = \sum_{i=1}^{3} Y_i - \frac{1}{2}X$

  d Find $Var(S)$.   **(2 marks)**

(E/P) **4** The thickness of paperback books can be **modelled** as a normal random variable with mean 2.1 cm and variance 0.39 cm². The thickness of hardback books can be modelled as a normal random variable with mean 4.0 cm and variance 1.56 cm². A small bookshelf is 30 cm long.

SKILLS
INTERPRETATION

  a Find the probability that a random sample of:

    i 15 paperback books can be placed side-by-side on the bookshelf

    ii 5 hardback and 5 paperback books can be placed side-by-side on the bookshelf. **(8 marks)**

  b Find the shortest length of bookshelf needed so that there is at least a 99% chance that it will hold a random sample of 15 paperback books.   **(3 marks)**

(E/P) **5** A sweet manufacturer produces two varieties of fruit sweet, *Xtras* and *Yummies*.

The masses, X and Y, in grams, of randomly selected *Xtras* and *Yummies* are such that:

      $X \sim N(30, 25)$ and $Y \sim N(32, 16)$

  a Find the probability that the mass of two randomly selected *Yummies* will differ by more than 5 g.   **(5 marks)**

One sweet of each variety is selected at random.

  b Find the probability that the *Yummy* sweet has a greater mass than the *Xtra*.   **(5 marks)**

A packet contains 6 *Xtras* and 4 *Yummies*.

  c Find the probability that the average mass of the sweets in the packet lies between 280 g and 330 g.   **(6 marks)**

E/P **6** A certain brand of biscuit is individually wrapped. The mass of a biscuit can be taken to be normally distributed with mean 75 g and standard deviation 5 g. The mass of an individual wrapping is normally distributed with mean 10 g and standard deviation 2 g. Six of these individually wrapped biscuits are then packed together. The mass of the packing material is a normal random variable with mean 40 g and standard deviation 3 g. Find, to 3 decimal places, the probability that the total mass of the packet lies between 535 g and 565 g.   **(7 marks)**

SKILLS
INTERPRETATION

E/P **7** The independent normal random variables X and Y have distributions N(10, 2²) and N(40, 3²) respectively (i.e. in the same order as mentioned before).
The random variable Q is defined as $Q = 2X + Y$

  a Find:

    i E(Q)   **(2 marks)**

    ii Var(Q)   **(3 marks)**

The random variables X_1, X_2, X_3, X_4, and X_5 are independent and all share the same distribution as X. The random variable R is defined as:

$$R = \sum_{i=1}^{5} X_i$$

  b i Find the distribution of R.   **ii** Find P($Q > R$).   **(7 marks)**

E/P **8** The usable capacity of the hard drive on a games console is normally distributed with mean 60 GB and standard deviation 2.5 GB. The amounts of storage required by games are modelled as being identically normally distributed with mean 5.5 GB and standard deviation 1.2 GB.

SKILLS
CRITICAL
THINKING

  a Chakrita wants to save 10 randomly chosen games onto her empty hard drive. Find the probability that they will fit.   **(8 marks)**

  b State one **assumption** you have made in your calculations, and comment on its validity.   **(1 mark)**

E/P **9** X_1, X_2, X_3 and X_4 are independent random variables, each with distribution N(4, 0.03). The random variables Y and Z are defined as:

    $Y = X_1 + X_2 + X_3$ $Z = 3X_4$

Find the probability that Y and Z differ by no more than 1.   **(5 marks)**

E/P **10** A builder purchases bags of sand in two sizes, large and small. Large bags have mass L kg and small bags have mass S kg. L and S are independent normally distributed random variables with distributions N(75, 5²) and N(40, 3²) respectively.

A large bag and a small bag of sand are chosen at random.

  a Find the probability that the mass of the small bag is more than half the mass of the large bag.   **(6 marks)**

The builder purchases 10 small bags of sand. The total mass of these bags is represented by the random variable M.

  b Find P($|M - 400| < 5$)   **(5 marks)**

Challenge

SKILLS
INNOVATION

For independent random variables X and Y, $E(XY) = E(X)E(Y)$.

Use this result to prove that if X and Y are independent random variables, then $\text{Var}(X + Y) = \text{Var}(X) + \text{Var}(Y)$.

Hint You may make use of the fact that for any two random variables, $E(X + Y) = E(X) + E(Y)$.

Summary of key points

1 If X and Y are two independent random variables, then:
  - $E(X + Y) = E(X) + E(Y)$
  - $E(X - Y) = E(X) - E(Y)$

2 If X and Y are two independent random variables, then:
  - $\text{Var}(X + Y) = \text{Var}(X) + \text{Var}(Y)$
  - $\text{Var}(X - Y) = \text{Var}(X) + \text{Var}(Y)$

3 If X and Y are two independent random variables, then:
  - $E(aX + bY) = aE(X) + bE(Y)$
  - $E(aX - bY) = aE(X) - bE(Y)$

4 If X and Y are two independent random variables, then:
  - $\text{Var}(aX + bY) = a^2\text{Var}(X) + b^2\text{Var}(Y)$
  - $\text{Var}(aX - bY) = a^2\text{Var}(X) + b^2\text{Var}(Y)$

5 A linear combination of normally distributed random variables is also normally distributed.

6 If X and Y are independent random variables with $X \sim N(\mu_1, \sigma_1^2)$ and $Y \sim N(\mu_2, \sigma_2^2)$, then:
  - $aX + bY \sim N(a\mu_1 + b\mu_2, a^2\sigma_1^2 + b^2\sigma_2^2)$
  - $aX - bY \sim N(a\mu_1 - b\mu_2, a^2\sigma_1^2 + b^2\sigma_2^2)$

7 If $X_1, X_2, \ldots, X_n$ are independent identically distributed random variables with $X_i \sim N(\mu, \sigma^2)$, then $\sum_{i=1}^{n} X_i \sim N(n\mu, n\sigma^2)$

3 ESTIMATORS AND CONFIDENCE INTERVALS

Learning objectives

After completing this chapter you should be able to:

Prior knowledge check

1 The independent normal random variables A and B have distributions $N(6, 2^2)$ and $N(7, 3^2)$ respectively.
   a Find $P(A > B)$.
   The random variable X is defined as $X = 3A + B$.
   b Find the distribution of X.   ← **Statistics 3 Section 2.1**

In large-scale production processes it might be impossible to test every component. Engineers use samples to determine ranges of values that are likely to contain population parameters such as the mean or variance.

3.1 Estimators, bias and standard error

In a large population (e.g. the number of trees in a forest), it would take too long or cost too much money to carry out a census (e.g. to record the height of every tree). In cases like this, **population parameters** such as the mean μ or the standard deviation σ are likely to be unknown.

In Chapter 1, you looked at methods of sampling that allow you to take a representative sample to estimate various population parameters.

A common way of estimating population parameters is to take a **random sample** from the population.

> **Links** A census observes every member of a population, whereas a sample is a selection of observations taken from a subset of the population. **← Statistics 2 Section 6.1**

- If X is a random variable, then a random sample of size n will consist of n **observations** of the random variable X. These are referred to as $X_1, X_2, X_3, \ldots, X_n$, where the X_i:
  - are independent random variables
  - each have the same distribution as X.

- A **statistic** T is defined as a function of the X_i that involves no other quantities, such as unknown population parameters.

> **Notation** X_i represents the ith observation of a sample. The value of the observation is denoted by x_i.

For example, $\overline{X}$, the sample mean, is a statistic, whereas $\sum_{i=1}^{n} \frac{X_i^2}{n} - \mu^2$ is not a statistic since it involves the unknown population parameter μ.

Example 1   SKILLS   REASONING/ARGUMENTATION

A sample $X_1, X_2, \ldots, X_n$ is taken from a population with unknown population parameters μ and σ. State whether or not each of the following are statistics.

a $\dfrac{X_1 + X_3 + X_5}{3}$

b $\max(X_1, X_2, \ldots, X_n)$

c $\displaystyle\sum_{i=1}^{n} \left(\frac{X_i - \mu}{\sigma} \right)^2$

a $\dfrac{X_1 + X_3 + X_5}{3}$ is a statistic. → It is only a function of the sample $X_1, X_2, \ldots, X_n$. A statistic need not involve all members of the sample.

b $\max(X_1, X_2, \ldots, X_n)$ is a statistic. → It is only a function of the sample $X_1, X_2, \ldots, X_n$.

c $\displaystyle\sum_{i=1}^{n} \left(\frac{X_i - \mu}{\sigma} \right)^2$ is not a statistic. → The function contains μ and σ.

Since it is possible to repeat the process of taking a sample, the specific value of a statistic T will be different for each sample. If all possible samples are taken, these values will form a probability distribution called the **sampling distribution** of T.

- **The sampling distribution of a statistic T is the probability distribution of T.**

If the distribution of the population is known, then the sampling distribution of a statistic can sometimes be found.

Example 2

The masses, in grams, of boxes of apples are normally distributed with a mean μ and standard deviation 4. A random sample of size 25 is taken and the statistics R and T are calculated as follows:

$$R = X_{25} - X_1 \text{ and } T = X_1 + X_2 + \dots + X_{25}$$

Find the distributions of R and T.

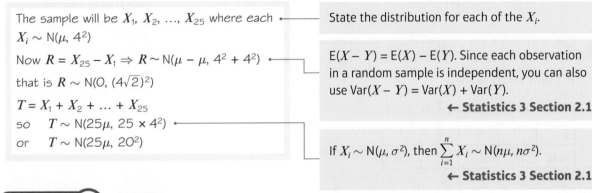

The sample will be $X_1, X_2, \dots, X_{25}$ where each
$X_i \sim N(\mu, 4^2)$

Now $R = X_{25} - X_1 \Rightarrow R \sim N(\mu - \mu, 4^2 + 4^2)$

that is $R \sim N(0, (4\sqrt{2})^2)$

$T = X_1 + X_2 + \dots + X_{25}$

so $T \sim N(25\mu, 25 \times 4^2)$

or $T \sim N(25\mu, 20^2)$

State the distribution for each of the X_i.

$E(X - Y) = E(X) - E(Y)$. Since each observation in a random sample is independent, you can also use $Var(X - Y) = Var(X) + Var(Y)$.

← **Statistics 3 Section 2.1**

If $X_i \sim N(\mu, \sigma^2)$, then $\sum_{i=1}^{n} X_i \sim N(n\mu, n\sigma^2)$.

← **Statistics 3 Section 2.1**

Example 3   **SKILLS**   CREATIVITY

In a bag that contains a large number of counters, the number 0 is written on 60% of the counters, and the number 1 is written on the other 40%.

a Find the population mean μ and population variance σ^2 of the values shown on the counters.

A simple random sample of size 3 is taken from this population.

b List all the possible observations from this sample.

c Find the sampling distribution for the mean

$$\overline{X} = \frac{X_1 + X_2 + X_3}{3}$$

where X_1, X_2 and X_3 are the values shown on the three counters in the sample.

d Hence find $E(\overline{X})$ and $Var(\overline{X})$.

e Find the sampling distribution for the sample **mode** M.

f Hence find $E(M)$ and $Var(M)$.

a If X represents the value shown on a randomly chosen counter, then X has distribution:

x	0	1
$P(X = x)$	$\frac{3}{5}$	$\frac{2}{5}$

$\mu = E(X) = \sum x P(X = x) = 0 + \frac{2}{5} \Rightarrow \mu = \frac{2}{5}$

$\sigma^2 = Var(X) = \sum x^2 P(X = x) - \mu^2 = 0 + 1^2 \times \frac{2}{5} - \frac{4}{25} \Rightarrow \sigma^2 = \frac{6}{25}$

b The possible observations are

(0, 0, 0)

(1, 0, 0) (0, 1, 0) (0, 0, 1)

(1, 1, 0) (1, 0, 1) (0, 1, 1)

(1, 1, 1)

> List these systematically.

c $P(\overline{X} = 0) = \left(\frac{3}{5}\right)^3 = \frac{27}{125}$ *i.e.* the (0, 0, 0) case

$P\left(\overline{X} = \frac{1}{3}\right) = 3 \times \frac{2}{5} \times \left(\frac{3}{5}\right)^2 = \frac{54}{125}$ *i.e.* the (1, 0, 0), (0, 1, 0), (0, 0, 1) cases

$P\left(\overline{X} = \frac{2}{3}\right) = 3 \times \left(\frac{2}{5}\right)^2 \times \frac{3}{5} = \frac{36}{125}$ *i.e.* the (1, 1, 0), (1, 0, 1), (0, 1, 1) cases

$P(\overline{X} = 1) = \left(\frac{2}{5}\right)^3 = \frac{8}{125}$ *i.e.* the (1, 1, 1) case

> Since the sample is random, the observations are independent. So to find the probability of case (1, 0, 0) you can multiply the probabilities $P(X_1 = 1) \times P(X_2 = 0) \times P(X_3 = 0)$. Remember that each X_i has the same distribution as X.
> ← **Statistics 2 Chapter 1**

So the distribution for $\overline{X}$ is

$\overline{x}$	0	$\frac{1}{3}$	$\frac{2}{3}$	1
$p(\overline{x})$	$\frac{27}{125}$	$\frac{54}{125}$	$\frac{36}{125}$	$\frac{8}{125}$

d $E(\overline{X}) = 0 + \frac{1}{3} \times \frac{54}{125} + \frac{2}{3} \times \frac{36}{125} + 1 \times \frac{8}{125} = \frac{18 + 24 + 8}{125} = \frac{2}{5}$

$Var(\overline{X}) = 0 + \frac{1}{9} \times \frac{54}{125} + \frac{4}{9} \times \frac{36}{125} + 1 \times \frac{8}{125} - \frac{4}{25} = \frac{6 + 16 + 8}{125} - \frac{20}{125} = \frac{2}{25}$

e The sample mode can take values 0 or 1.

$P(M = 0) = \frac{27}{125} + \frac{54}{125} = \frac{81}{125}$ *i.e.* cases (0, 0, 0), (1, 0, 0), (0, 1, 0), (0, 0, 1)

and $P(M = 1) = \frac{44}{125}$ *i.e.* the other cases

so the distribution of M is

m	0	1
$p(m)$	$\frac{81}{125}$	$\frac{44}{125}$

> **Notation** Notice that $E(\overline{X}) = \mu$ but $E(M) \neq \mu$ and that neither $E(\overline{X})$ nor $E(M)$ is equal to the population mode, which is of course zero as 60% of the counters have a zero on them.

f $E(M) = 0 + 1 \times \frac{44}{125} = \frac{44}{125}$

and $Var(M) = 0 + 1 \times \frac{44}{125} - \left(\frac{44}{125}\right)^2 = 0.228$

- **A statistic that is used to estimate a population parameter is called an estimator and the particular value of the estimator generated from the sample taken is called an estimate.**

You need to be able to determine how **reliable** these sample statistics are as estimators for the **corresponding** population parameters.

Since all the X_i are random variables having the same mean and variance as the population, you can sometimes find expected values of a statistic T, $E(T)$. This will tell you what the 'average' value of the statistic should be.

Example **4** 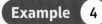 **SKILLS**   **ANALYSIS**

A random sample $X_1, X_2, \ldots, X_n$ is taken from a population with $X \sim N(\mu, \sigma^2)$.

Show that $E(\overline{X}) = \mu$.

$$\overline{X} = \frac{1}{n}(X_1 + \ldots + X_n)$$

$$E(\overline{X}) = \frac{1}{n}E(X_1 + \ldots + X_n) \quad\longleftarrow\quad \text{Use } E(aX) = aE(X)$$

$$= \frac{1}{n}(E(X_1) + \ldots + E(X_n)) \quad\longleftarrow\quad E(X + Y) = E(X) + E(Y)$$

$$= \frac{1}{n}(\mu + \ldots + \mu)$$

$$= \frac{n\mu}{n}$$

$$E(\overline{X}) = \mu$$

This example shows that if you use the sample mean as an estimator of the population mean, then 'on average' it will give the correct value.

This is an important property for an estimator to have. You say that $\overline{X}$ is an **unbiased estimator** of μ. A specific value of $\overline{x}$ will be an unbiased estimate for μ.

- If a statistic T is used as an estimator for a population parameter θ and $E(T) = \theta$, then T is an unbiased estimator for θ.

In Example 3, you found two statistics based on samples of size 3 from a population of counters. The two statistics that you calculated were the sample mean $\overline{X}$ and the sample mode M. You could use either of them as estimators for μ, the population mean, but you saw that $E(\overline{X}) = \mu$ and $E(M) \neq \mu$. In this case, if you wanted an unbiased estimator for μ, you would choose the sample mean $\overline{X}$ rather than the sample mode M, which we would call a biased estimator. How about an estimator for the population mode? Neither of the statistics that you calculated had the property of being unbiased since $E(\overline{X}) = \mu = \frac{2}{5}$ and $E(M) = \frac{44}{125}$, whereas the population mode was 0.

The **bias** is the expected value of the estimator minus the **parameter** of the population it is estimating.

- If a statistic T is used as an estimator for a population parameter θ, then the bias is $E(T) - \theta$.

In this case the bias is $\frac{44}{125}$

- For an unbiased estimator, the bias is 0.

In Example 4, the mean of a sample was an unbiased estimator for the population mean. If you take a sample X_1 of size 1 from a population with mean μ and variance σ^2, then the sample mean is $\overline{X} = X_1$, because there is only one value. So $E(\overline{X}) = E(X_1) = \mu$.

If you wanted to find an estimator for the **population variance**, you might try using the variance of the sample, $V = \dfrac{\sum(X_i - \overline{X})^2}{n}$

For our sample X_1 of size 1, the variance of the sample will be $\dfrac{(X_1 - \overline{X})^2}{1} = (X_1 - X_1)^2 = 0$

> **Hint** In general, the variance of a sample will be an **underestimate** for the variance of the population. This is because the statistic $\dfrac{\sum(X_i - \overline{X})^2}{n}$ uses the sample mean $\overline{X}$ rather than the population mean μ, and on average the sample observations will be closer to $\overline{X}$ than to μ.

So for a sample of size 1, $E(V) = 0 \neq \sigma^2$. This illustrates that the variance of the sample is not an unbiased estimator for the variance of the population.

You can use a slightly different statistic, called the **sample variance**, as an unbiased estimator for the population variance.

- An unbiased estimator for σ^2 is given by the sample variance S^2 where:

$$S^2 = \frac{1}{n-1} \sum_{i=1}^{n} (X_i - \overline{X})^2$$

> **Notation** S^2 is the estimator (a random variable), and s^2 is the estimate (an observation from this random variable).

There are several ways to calculate the value of s^2 for a particular sample:

$$s^2 = \frac{1}{n-1} \sum_{i=1}^{n} (x_i - \overline{x})^2$$

$$= \frac{S_{xx}}{n-1}$$

$$= \frac{n}{n-1}\left(\frac{\sum x^2}{n} - \overline{x}^2\right)$$

$$= \frac{1}{n-1}\left(\sum x^2 - n\overline{x}^2\right)$$

> **Links** You can use the equivalence of these forms to show that s^2 is an unbiased estimate for σ^2.
> → **Exercise 3A Challenge**

The form that you use will depend on the information that you are given in the question.

Although a sample of size 1 can be used as an unbiased estimator of μ, a single observation from a population will not provide a useful estimate of the population mean. You need some way of distinguishing between the **quality** of different unbiased estimators.

Example **5** **SKILLS** **ANALYSIS**

A random sample $X_1, X_2, \ldots, X_n$ is taken from a population with $X \sim N(\mu, \sigma^2)$.

Show that $\text{Var}(\overline{X}) = \dfrac{\sigma^2}{n}$

$$\overline{X} = \frac{1}{n}(X_1 + \ldots + X_n)$$

$$\text{Var}(\overline{X}) = \frac{1}{n^2}\text{Var}(X_1 + \ldots + X_n) \quad\longleftarrow \quad \text{Use } \text{Var}(aX) = a^2\text{Var}(X)$$

$$= \frac{1}{n^2}(\text{Var}(X_1) + \ldots + \text{Var}(X_n)) \quad\longleftarrow \quad \text{Use } \text{Var}(X + Y) = \text{Var}(X) + \text{Var}(Y)$$

$$= \frac{1}{n^2}(\sigma^2 + \ldots + \sigma^2)$$

$$= \frac{n\sigma^2}{n^2}$$

$$\text{Var}(\overline{X}) = \frac{\sigma^2}{n}$$

One reason that the **sample mean** is used as an estimator for μ is that the variance of the estimator $\text{Var}(\overline{X}) = \dfrac{\sigma^2}{n}$ decreases as n increases. For larger values of n, the value of an estimate is more likely to be close to the population mean. So, a larger value of n will result in a **better** estimator.

- The standard deviation of an estimator is called the standard error of the estimator.

When you are using the sample mean $\overline{X}$ you can use the following result for the standard error.

- Standard error of $\overline{X} = \dfrac{\sigma}{\sqrt{n}}$ or $\dfrac{s}{\sqrt{n}}$

Watch out Although in general $\sigma \neq s$, you can use the second version of this standard error in situations where you **do not know** the population standard deviation.

Example 6   **SKILLS** ADAPTIVE LEARNING

The table below summarises the number of breakdowns X on a busy road on 30 randomly chosen days.

Number of breakdowns	2	3	4	5	6	7	8	9
Number of days	3	5	4	3	5	4	4	2

a Calculate unbiased estimates of the mean and variance of the number of breakdowns.

Twenty more days were randomly sampled, and this sample had $\overline{x} = 6.0$ days and $s^2 = 5.0$

b Treating the 50 results as a single sample, obtain further unbiased estimates of the population mean and variance.

c Find the standard error of this new estimate of the mean.

d Estimate the size of sample required to achieve a standard error of less than 0.25

a By calculator:

$$\sum x = 160 \text{ and } \sum x^2 = 990$$

So $\hat{\mu} = \overline{x} = \dfrac{160}{30} = 5.33$

and $\hat{\sigma}^2 = s_x^2 = \dfrac{990 - 30\overline{x}^2}{29}$

$$= 4.71 \text{ (3 s.f.)}$$

b New sample: $\overline{y} = 6.0 \Rightarrow \sum y = 20 \times 6.0 = 120$

$$s_y^2 = 5.0 \Rightarrow \dfrac{\sum y^2 - 20 \times 6^2}{19} = 5$$

So $\sum y^2 = 5 \times 19 + 20 \times 36$

$\Rightarrow \quad \sum y^2 = 815$

So the combined sample (w) of size 50 has

$$\sum w = 160 + 120 = 280$$
$$\sum w^2 = 990 + 815 = 1805$$

Notation 'Hat' notation is used to describe an estimate of a parameter. For example: $\hat{\sigma}^2$ represents an estimate for the population variance σ^2. $\hat{\mu}$ represents an estimate for the population mean μ.

Use $s^2 = \dfrac{1}{n-1}\left(\sum x^2 - n\overline{x}^2\right)$ since you have values for $\sum x^2$ and $\overline{x}$.

Problem-solving

First you need to use the formulae for $\overline{y}$ and s_y^2 to find $\sum y$ and $\sum y^2$.

Now combine with $\sum x$ and $\sum x^2$. Let the combined variable be w.

Hint You can use your calculator to find unbiased estimates of the mean and variance but you should show your working in the exam.

Then the combined estimate of μ is

$$\bar{w} = \frac{280}{50} = 5.6$$

and the estimate for σ^2 is

$$s_w^2 = \frac{1805 - 50 \times 5.6^2}{49}$$

$$\Rightarrow s_w^2 = 4.8367... = 4.84 \text{ (3 s.f.)}$$

c   The best estimate of σ^2 will be s_w^2 since it is based on a larger sample than s_x^2 or s_y^2.

So the standard error is $\dfrac{s_w}{\sqrt{50}} = \sqrt{\dfrac{4.836...}{50}}$ ──── Use the $\dfrac{s}{\sqrt{n}}$ formula for standard error.

$$= 0.311 \text{ (3 s.f.)}$$

d   To achieve a standard error < 0.25 you require

$$\sqrt{\frac{4.836...}{n}} < 0.25$$ ──── You do not know the value for σ so you will have to use your best estimate of it, namely s_w.

$$\Rightarrow \quad \sqrt{n} > \frac{\sqrt{4.836...}}{0.25}$$

$$\sqrt{n} > 8.797...$$

$$\Rightarrow \quad n > 77.38...$$

So we need a sample size of at least 78.

We have seen that for the independent observations $X_i \sim N(\mu, \sigma^2)$, we can evaluate the statistic

$$\bar{X} = \frac{X_1 + X_2 + \cdots + X_n}{n}$$

In Example 4, we saw that

$$E(\bar{X}) = \mu$$

and in Example 5 that

$$\text{Var}(\bar{X}) = \frac{\sigma^2}{n}$$

Since X is normally distributed and each X_i is an independent observation, $\bar{X}$ must also be normally distributed, so we can create the distribution of the sample mean.

If $X_i \sim N(\mu, \sigma^2)$ then $\bar{X} \sim N\left(\mu, \dfrac{\sigma^2}{n}\right)$, where $\dfrac{\sigma}{\sqrt{n}}$ is the standard error.

Example 7

Ten independent observations from $X \sim N(15, 3^2)$ are taken.

a   State the distribution of the sample mean.

b   Find $P(\bar{X} < 14)$

a Since X is normally distributed and the observations are independent,

$$E(\overline{X}) = \mu = 15$$

and

$$Var(\overline{X}) = \frac{3^2}{10} = 0.9$$

Therefore,

$$\overline{X} \sim N(15, 0.9)$$

b Standardising:

$$P(\overline{X} < 13) = P\left(Z < \frac{14 - 15}{0.9}\right)$$

We use $z = \dfrac{\overline{x} - \mu}{\frac{\sigma}{\sqrt{n}}}$ to standardise.

$$P(Z < -1.11...)$$

Using the tables on page 135.

$$= 1 - P(Z < 1.11...)$$
$$= 1 - 0.8665$$
$$= 0.1335$$

Exercise 3A **SKILLS** PROBLEM-SOLVING

1 The lengths of nails produced by a certain machine are normally distributed with mean μ and standard deviation σ. A random sample of 10 nails is taken and their lengths $X_1, X_2, X_3, \ldots, X_{10}$ are measured.

SKILLS
INTERPRETATION

   i Write down the distributions of the following:

   a $\displaystyle\sum_{1}^{10} X_i$ **b** $\dfrac{2X_1 + 3X_{10}}{5}$ **c** $\displaystyle\sum_{1}^{10}(X_i - \mu)$

   d $\overline{X}$ **e** $\displaystyle\sum_{1}^{5} X_i - \sum_{6}^{10} X_i$ **f** $\displaystyle\sum_{1}^{10}\left(\dfrac{X_i - \mu}{\sigma}\right)$

   ii State which of the above are statistics.

2 A large bag of coins contains 1 cent, 5 cent and 10 cent coins in the ratio $2 : 2 : 1$

   a Find the mean μ and the variance σ^2 for the value of coins in this population.

   A random sample of two coins is taken and their values X_1 and X_2 are recorded.

   b List all the possible observations from this sample.

   c Find the sampling distribution for the mean $\overline{X} = \dfrac{X_1 + X_2}{2}$

   d Hence show that $E(\overline{X}) = \mu$ and $Var(\overline{X}) = \dfrac{\sigma^2}{2}$

3 Find unbiased estimates of the mean and variance of the populations from which the following random samples have been taken.

   a 21.3   19.6   18.5   22.3   17.4   16.3   18.9   17.6   18.7   16.5   19.3   21.8   20.1   22.0

   b 1   2   5   1   6   4   1   3   2   8   5   6   2   4   3   1

   c 120.4   230.6   356.1   129.8   185.6   147.6   258.3   329.7   249.3

   d 0.862   0.754   0.459   0.473   0.493   0.681   0.743   0.469   0.538   0.361

4 Find unbiased estimates of the mean and the variance of the populations from which random samples with the following summaries have been taken.

   a $n = 120$ $\sum x = 4368$ $\sum x^2 = 162\,466$

   b $n = 30$ $\sum x = 270$ $\sum x^2 = 2546$

   c $n = 1037$ $\sum x = 1140.7$ $\sum x^2 = 1278.08$

   d $n = 15$ $\sum x = 168$ $\sum x^2 = 1913$

(E) 5 The concentrations, in mg per litre, of an element in 7 randomly chosen samples of water from a spring were:

      240.8   237.3   236.7   236.6   234.2   233.9   232.5

   a Explain what is meant by an unbiased estimator.   **(1 mark)**

   b Determine unbiased estimates of the mean and the variance of the concentration of the element per litre of water from the spring.   **(4 marks)**

(E) 6 A sample of size 6 is taken from a population that is normally distributed with mean 10 and standard deviation 2.

   a Find the probability that the sample mean is greater than 12.   **(3 marks)**

   b State, with a reason, if your answer is an approximation.   **(1 mark)**

7 A machine fills cartons in such a way that the amount of drink in each carton is distributed normally with a mean of $40\,\text{cm}^3$ and a standard deviation of $1.5\,\text{cm}^3$.

   A sample of four cartons is examined.

   a Find the probability that the mean amount of drink is more than $40.5\,\text{cm}^3$.

   A sample of 49 cartons is examined.

   b Find the probability that the mean amount of drink is more than $40.5\,\text{cm}^3$ on this occasion.

(E) 8 Cartons of orange juice are filled by a machine. A sample of 10 cartons selected at random from the production line contained the following quantities of orange juice (in ml).

      201.2   205.0   209.1   202.3   204.6   206.4   210.1   201.9   203.7   207.3

   Calculate unbiased estimates of the mean and variance of the population from which this sample was taken.   **(4 marks)**

9 A manufacturer of self-build furniture required bolts of two lengths, 5 cm and 10 cm, in the ratio $2:1$ respectively.

   a Find the mean μ and the variance σ^2 for the lengths of bolts in this population.

   A random sample of three bolts is selected from a large box containing bolts in the required ratio.

   b List all the possible observations from this sample.

   c Find the sampling distribution for the mean $\overline{X}$.

   d Hence find $E(\overline{X})$ and $Var(\overline{X})$.

    e Find the sampling distribution for the mode M.

    f Hence find $E(M)$ and $Var(M)$.

    g Find the bias when M is used as an estimator of the population mode.

10 A biased six-sided dice has probability p of landing on a six.

    Every day, for a period of 25 days, the dice is rolled 10 times and the number of sixes X is recorded, giving rise to a sample X_1, X_2, ..., X_{25}.

    a Write down $E(X)$ in terms of p.

    b Show that the sample mean $\overline{X}$ is a biased estimator of p and find the bias.

    c Suggest a suitable unbiased estimator of p.

11 The random variable $X \sim U[-\alpha, \alpha]$.

    a Find $E(X)$ and $E(X^2)$.

    A random sample X_1, X_2, X_3 is taken and the statistic $Y = X_1^2 + X_2^2 + X_3^2$ is calculated.

    b Show that Y is an unbiased estimator of α^2.

12 Jiaqi and Mei Mei each independently took a random sample of students at their school and asked them how much money, in RMB, they earned last week. Jiaqi used his sample of size 20 to obtain unbiased estimates of the mean and variance of the amount earned by a student at their college last week. He obtained values of $\overline{x} = 15.5$ and $s_x^2 = 8.0$

    Mei Mei's sample of size 30 can be summarised as $\sum y = 486$ and $\sum y^2 = 8222$

    a Use Mei Mei's sample to find unbiased estimates of μ and σ^2. **(2 marks)**

    b Combine the samples and use all 50 observations to obtain further unbiased estimates of μ and σ^2. **(4 marks)**

    c Explain what is meant by standard error. **(1 mark)**

    d Find the standard error of the mean for each of these estimates of μ. **(2 marks)**

    e Comment on which estimate of μ you would prefer to use. **(1 mark)**

13 A factory worker checks a random sample of 20 bottles from a production line in order to estimate the mean volume of bottles (in cm³) from this production run. The 20 values can be summarised as $\sum x = 1300$ and $\sum x^2 = 84\,685$.

    a Use this sample to find unbiased estimates of μ and σ^2. **(2 marks)**

    A factory manager knows from experience that the standard deviation of volumes on this process, σ, should be 3 cm³ and he wishes to have an estimate of μ that has a standard error of less than 0.5 cm³.

    b Recommend a sample size for the manager, showing working to support your recommendation. **(2 marks)**

    c Does your recommended sample size guarantee a standard error of less than 0.5 cm³? Give a reason for your answer. **(1 mark)**

    The manager takes a further sample of size 16 and finds $\sum x = 1060$.

    d Combine the two samples to obtain a revised estimate of μ. **(2 marks)**

(E) **14** After growing for 10 weeks in a greenhouse, the heights of certain plants have a standard deviation of 2.6 cm. Find the smallest sample that must be taken for the standard error of the mean to be less than 0.5 cm.   **(3 marks)**

(E) **15** The hardness of a new type of material was determined by measuring the depth of the hole made by a heavy pointed device.

The following observations in tenths of a millimetre were obtained:

4.7   5.2   5.4   4.8   4.5   4.9   4.5   5.1   5.0   4.8

  a Estimate the mean depth of hole for this material.   **(1 mark)**

  b Find the standard error for your estimate.   **(2 marks)**

  c Estimate the size of sample required so that in future the standard error of the mean should be just less than 0.05   **(3 marks)**

(P) **16** To work for a company, applicants need to complete a medical test. The probability of each applicant passing the test is p, independent of any other applicant. The medicals are carried out over two days and on the first day n applicants are seen, and on the next day $2n$ are seen. Let X_1 represent the number of applicants who pass the test on the first day and let X_2 represent the number who pass on the second day.

  a Write down $E(X_1)$, $E(X_2)$, $Var(X_1)$ and $Var(X_2)$.

  b Show that $\dfrac{X_1}{n}$ and $\dfrac{X_2}{2n}$ are both unbiased estimates of p and state, giving a reason, which you would prefer to use.

  c Show that $X = \dfrac{1}{2}\left(\dfrac{X_1}{n} + \dfrac{X_2}{2n}\right)$ is an unbiased estimator of p.

  d Show that $Y = \left(\dfrac{X_1 + X_2}{3n}\right)$ is an unbiased estimator of p.

  e Which of the statistics $\dfrac{X_1}{n}$, $\dfrac{X_2}{2n}$, X or Y is the best estimator of p?

The statistic $T = \left(\dfrac{2X_1 + X_2}{3n}\right)$ is proposed as an estimator of p.

  f Find the bias.

(P) **17** In a bag that contains a large number of counters, the number 0 is written on 40% of the counters, the number 1 is written on 20% of the counters, and the number 2 is written on the remaining 40% of the counters.

  a Find the mean μ and the variance σ^2 for this population of counters.

A random sample of size 3 is taken from the bag.

  b List all the possible observations from this sample.

  c Find the sampling distribution for the mean $\overline{X}$.

  d Find $E(\overline{X})$ and $Var(\overline{X})$.

  e Find the sampling distribution for the **median** N.

  f Hence, find $E(N)$ and $Var(N)$.

  g Show that N is an unbiased estimator of μ.

  h Explain which estimator, $\overline{X}$ or N, you would choose as an estimator of μ.

SKILLS

ANALYSIS

Challenge

a Show that $\dfrac{1}{n-1}\displaystyle\sum_{i=1}^{n}(x_i-\bar{x})^2 = \dfrac{1}{n-1}\left(\sum x^2 - n\bar{x}^2\right)$

b Hence, or otherwise, show that s^2 is an unbiased estimate for the population variance σ^2.

3.2 Confidence intervals

The value of $\widehat{\theta}$, which is an estimator of θ, is found from a sample. It is used as an unbiased estimate for the population parameter θ and is very unlikely to be exactly equal to θ.

There is no way of establishing, from the sample data only, how close the estimate is.

Instead, you can form a **confidence interval** for θ.

- A confidence interval (C.I.) for a population parameter θ is a range of values defined so that there is a specific probability that the true value of the parameter lies within that range.

For example, you could establish a 90% confidence interval, or a 95% confidence interval.

A 95% confidence interval is an interval such that there is a 0.95 probability that the interval contains θ.

Different samples will generate different confidence intervals since estimates for the parameter will change based on the data in the sample and the sample size.

Watch out The population parameter θ is fixed, so you cannot talk about its value in probabilistic terms.

$$\overline{X} \sim \text{N}\left(\mu, \frac{\sigma^2}{n}\right)$$

Hence, if you know the population standard deviation, you can establish a confidence interval for the population mean μ using the standardised normal distribution.

Example 8

Given that X is normally distributed, show that a 95% confidence interval for μ, based on a sample of size n, is given by:

$$\left(\bar{x} - 1.96 \times \frac{\sigma}{\sqrt{n}}, \bar{x} + 1.96 \times \frac{\sigma}{\sqrt{n}}\right)$$

$\overline{X} \sim \text{N}\left(\mu, \dfrac{\sigma^2}{n}\right)$

and therefore

$Z = \dfrac{\overline{X} - \mu}{\dfrac{\sigma}{\sqrt{n}}} \sim \text{N}(0, 1^2)$

Using tables, you can see that for the N(0, 1²) distribution:

$P(Z > 1.9600) = P(Z < -1.9600) = 0.025$

and so 95% of the distribution is between −1.9600 and 1.9600

Problem-solving

You will need to use the **standardised** normal distribution N(0, 1²) to tackle problems like this.

If $X \sim \text{N}(\mu, \sigma^2)$ then $Z = \dfrac{X - \mu}{\sigma} \sim \text{N}(0, 1^2)$

← Statistics 1 Section 7.4

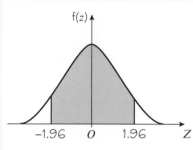

So $\quad P(-1.96 < Z < 1.96) = 0.95$

$\Rightarrow \quad P\left(-1.96 < \dfrac{\overline{X} - \mu}{\frac{\sigma}{\sqrt{n}}} < 1.96\right) = 0.95$

Look at the inequality inside the probability statement:

$$-1.96 \times \frac{\sigma}{\sqrt{n}} < \overline{X} - \mu < 1.96 \times \frac{\sigma}{\sqrt{n}}$$ ⟶ Start to isolate μ.

$$\overline{X} + 1.96 \times \frac{\sigma}{\sqrt{n}} > \mu > \overline{X} - 1.96 \times \frac{\sigma}{\sqrt{n}}$$ ⟶ Multiply by −1 and change the inequalities.

$$\overline{X} - 1.96 \times \frac{\sigma}{\sqrt{n}} < \mu < \overline{X} + 1.96 \times \frac{\sigma}{\sqrt{n}}$$

So the 95% confidence interval for μ is

$$\left(\overline{x} - 1.96 \times \frac{\sigma}{\sqrt{n}}, \ \overline{x} + 1.96 \times \frac{\sigma}{\sqrt{n}}\right)$$

Notation The upper and lower values of a confidence interval are sometimes called the **confidence limits**.

- The 95% confidence interval for μ is $\left(\overline{x} - 1.96 \times \dfrac{\sigma}{\sqrt{n}}, \ \overline{x} + 1.96 \times \dfrac{\sigma}{\sqrt{n}}\right)$

The value of 1.96 in the formula above is determined by the percentage points of the standardised normal distribution. By changing this value you can formulate confidence intervals with different levels of confidence.

For example, a 99% confidence interval would have 1.96 replaced by 2.5758, since that is the value of z such that $P(-z < Z < z) = 0.99$

Given one confidence interval, it is possible to calculate another.

Hint The choice of what confidence interval to use in a particular situation will depend on the problem involved but a value of 95% is commonly used if no other value is specified.

Interpreting confidence intervals

- First, it is important to remember that μ **is a fixed, but unknown**, number. Because of this, it cannot vary and does not have a distribution.
- Second, it is useful to remember that you base a 95% confidence interval on a probability statement about the normal distribution $Z \sim N(0, 1^2)$.
- Although you start by considering probabilities from the random variable Z, the final confidence interval does not tell you the probability that μ lies inside a fixed interval. Since μ is fixed, it is the confidence interval that varies (according to the value of $\overline{x}$).
- A 95% confidence interval tells you that the probability that the interval contains μ is 0.95

The diagram opposite shows the 95% confidence intervals calculated from different samples and also shows the position of μ. Suppose 20 samples of size 100 were taken, and 95% confidence intervals for μ were calculated for each sample. This would give 20 different confidence intervals, each based on one of the 20 different values of x.

If you assume that you know what the value of μ is, then you can plot each of these confidence intervals on a diagram similar to the one here; you would expect that 95% of these confidence intervals would contain the value μ, but about once in every 20 times you would get an interval which did not contain μ (marked * on the diagram).

The problem is that you never know whether the confidence interval calculated contains μ or not. However, 95% of the time (or 90%, or 99%, depending on the degree of confidence required), the interval will contain μ.

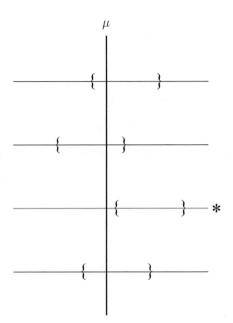

Example 9 　 SKILLS 　 ADAPTIVE LEARNING

A 90% confidence interval is given by (32.1, 42.7)

Calculate a 95% confidence interval.

$$\bar{x} + 1.6449 \times \frac{\sigma}{\sqrt{n}} = 42.7$$

Find $\bar{x}$ and $\frac{\sigma}{\sqrt{n}}$ by solving simultaneously.

$$\bar{x} - 1.6449 \times \frac{\sigma}{\sqrt{n}} = 32.1$$

$$2\bar{x} = 74.8$$

$$\bar{x} = 37.4$$

$$2 \times 1.6449 \times \frac{\sigma}{\sqrt{n}} = 10.6$$

$$\frac{\sigma}{\sqrt{n}} = \frac{10.6}{(2 \times 1.6499)} = 3.222...$$

A 95% confidence interval is:

$$\bar{x} \pm 1.96 \times \frac{\sigma}{\sqrt{n}}$$

The lower limit:

$$\bar{x} - 1.96 \times \frac{\sigma}{\sqrt{n}} = 37.4 - 1.96 \times 3.222... = 31.08$$

The upper limit:

$$\bar{x} - 1.96 \times \frac{\sigma}{\sqrt{n}} = 37.4 + 1.96 \times 3.222... = 43.72$$

A 95% confidence interval is

(31.08, 43.72)

Example (10)   **SKILLS**   REASONING/ARGUMENTATION

The breaking strains of string produced at a certain factory are normally distributed with standard deviation 1.5 kg. A sample of 100 lengths of string from a certain batch was tested and the mean breaking strain was 5.30 kg.

a Find a 95% confidence interval for the mean breaking strain of string in this batch.

The manufacturer becomes concerned if the lower 95% confidence limit falls below 5 kg. A sample of 80 lengths of string from another batch gave a mean breaking strain of 5.31 kg.

b Will the manufacturer be concerned?

a 95% confidence limits are:

$$\bar{x} \pm 1.96 \times \frac{\sigma}{\sqrt{n}} = 5.30 \pm 1.96 \times \frac{1.5}{\sqrt{100}}$$

So a 95% confidence interval is (5.006, 5.594)

b Lower 95% confidence limit is:

$$\bar{x} - 1.96 \times \frac{\sigma}{\sqrt{n}} = 5.31 - \frac{1.96 \times 1.5}{\sqrt{80}}$$

$$= 4.98$$

so the manufacturer will be concerned.

> Use the $\bar{x} \pm 1.96 \times \frac{\sigma}{\sqrt{n}}$ formula.

> **Notation**   In your exam you can define a confidence interval:
> - by giving the confidence limits, e.g. 5.30 ± 0.294
> - using interval notation, e.g. (5.006, 5.594) or [5.006, 5.594]
> - using inequalities, e.g. $5.006 < \mu < 5.594$

■ The width of a confidence interval is the difference between the upper confidence limit and the lower confidence limit. This is $2 \times z \times \frac{\sigma}{\sqrt{n}}$, where z is the relevant percentage point from the standardised normal distribution, for example 1.96, 1.6449, etc.

The greater the width, the less information you have about the population mean. There are three factors that affect the width: the value of σ, the size of the sample n and the degree of confidence required. In a particular example where σ and n are determined, the only factor you can change to alter the width is the level of confidence. A high level of confidence (e.g. 99%) will give a greater width than a lower level of confidence (e.g. 90%), and the statistician has to weigh up the advantages of high confidence against greater width when calculating a confidence interval.

Example (11)   **SKILLS**   PROBLEM-SOLVING

A random sample of size 25 is taken from a normal distribution with standard deviation 2.5. The mean of the sample is 17.8.

a Find a 99% C.I. for the population mean μ.

b What size sample is required to obtain a 99% C.I. with a width of at most 1.5?

c What confidence level would be associated with the interval based on the above sample of 25 but of width 1.5, i.e. (17.05, 18.55)?

a 99% confidence limits are:

$$\bar{x} \pm 2.5758 \times \frac{\sigma}{\sqrt{n}} = 17.8 \pm 2.5758 \times \frac{2.5}{\sqrt{25}}$$

So a 99% confidence interval is (16.51, 19.09)

> Use the table on page 136 to find 2.5758

b Width of 99% C.I. is $2 \times 2.5758 \times \frac{2.5}{\sqrt{n}}$

> Use the $2 \times z \times \frac{\sigma}{\sqrt{n}}$ formula or the definition for the width.

so you require $1.5 > \dfrac{12.879...}{\sqrt{n}}$

i.e. $n > 73.719...$

so you need $n = 74$

c A width of $1.5 \Rightarrow 1.5 = 2 \times z \times \dfrac{2.5}{\sqrt{25}}$

$$z = 1.5$$

From the table on page 135 you find that

$$P(Z < 1.5) = 0.9332$$

and so $P(Z > 1.5) = P(Z < -1.5)$

$$= 1 - 0.9332$$
$$= 0.0668$$

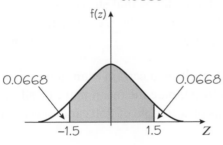

So the confidence level is

$100 \times (1 - 2 \times 0.0668) = 86.6\%$

> The percentage of the confidence interval is given by the area between $z = \pm 1.5$

Exercise 3B   SKILLS   PROBLEM-SOLVING

1 A random sample of size 9 is taken from a normal distribution with variance 36.
The sample mean is 128.

   a Find a 95% confidence interval for the mean μ of the distribution.

   b Find a 99% confidence interval for the mean μ of the distribution.

2 A random sample of size 25 is taken from a normal distribution with standard deviation 4.
The sample mean is 85.

   a Find a 90% confidence interval for the mean μ of the distribution.

   b Find a 95% confidence interval for the mean μ of the distribution.

3 A 95% confidence interval is given by (25.61, 27.19)
Calculate a 99% confidence interval.

4 A normal distribution has standard deviation 15. Estimate the sample size required if the following confidence intervals for the mean should have width of less than 2.

  a 90%   **b** 95%   **c** 99%

(E/P) 5 A railway company is studying the number of seconds that express trains are late to arrive. Previous surveys have shown that the times are normally distributed and that the standard deviation is 50. A random sample of 200 trains was selected and gave rise to a mean of 310 seconds late.

  a Find a 90% confidence interval for μ, the mean number of seconds that express trains are late.   **(3 marks)**

Five different independent random samples of 200 trains are selected, and each sample is used to generate a different 90% confidence interval for μ.

  b Find the probability that exactly three of these confidence intervals contain μ.   **(2 marks)**

Hint Use a suitable **binomial distribution**.

(E/P) 6 Amy is investigating the total distance travelled by vans in current use. The standard deviation can be assumed to be 15 000 km. In a random sample, 80 vans were stopped and their mean distance travelled was found to be 75 872 km.

Amy suspects that the population is normally distributed, but claims that she can still use the normal distribution to find a confidence interval for μ. Find a 90% confidence interval for the mean distance travelled by vans in current use.   **(3 marks)**

(E/P) 7 It is known that each year the standard deviation of the marks in a certain examination is 13.5 but the mean mark μ will fluctuate. An examiner wants to estimate the mean mark of all the candidates on the examination but he only has the marks of a sample of 250 candidates, which gives a sample mean of 68.4

  a What assumption about the candidates must the examiner make in order to use this sample mean to calculate a confidence interval for μ?   **(1 mark)**

  b Assuming that the above assumption is justified, calculate a 95% confidence interval for μ.   **(3 marks)**

Later, the examiner discovers that the actual value of μ was 65.3

  c What conclusions might the examiner draw about his sample?   **(2 marks)**

(E/P) 8 A student calculated 95% and 99% confidence intervals for the mean μ of a certain population but failed to label them. The two intervals were (22.7, 27.3) and (23.2, 26.8).

  a State, with a reason, which interval is the 95% one.   **(1 mark)**

  b Estimate the standard error of the mean in this case.   **(2 marks)**

  c What was the student's unbiased estimate of the mean μ in this case?   **(2 marks)**

(E) 9 The director of a company has asked for a survey to estimate the mean expenditure of customers on electrical appliances. In a random sample, 100 people were questioned and the research team presented the director with a 95% confidence interval of ($128.14, $141.86).

The director says that this interval is too wide and wants a confidence interval of total width $10.

  a Using the same value of $\bar{x}$, find the confidence limits in this case.   **(3 marks)**

  b Find the level of confidence for the interval in part **a**.   **(2 marks)**

The managing director is still not happy and now wishes to know how large a sample would be required to obtain a 95% confidence interval of total width no greater than $10.

  c Find the smallest size of sample that will **satisfy** this request.   **(3 marks)**

(E) **10** A factory produces steel sheets whose masses are known to be normally distributed with a standard deviation of 2.4 kg. A random sample of 36 sheets had a mean mass of 31.4 kg. Find 99% confidence limits for the population mean.   **(3 marks)**

(E) **11** A machine is set up to pour liquid into cartons in such a way that the amount of liquid poured on each occasion is normally distributed with a standard deviation of 20 ml.

Find 99% confidence limits for the mean amount of liquid poured if a random sample of 40 cartons had an average content of 266 ml.   **(3 marks)**

(E/P) **12** **a** The error made when a certain instrument is used to measure the body length of a butterfly of a particular species is known to be normally distributed with mean 0 and standard deviation 1 mm. Calculate, to 3 decimal places, the probability that the size of the error made when the instrument is used once is less than 0.4 mm.   **(2 marks)**

    b Given that the body length of a butterfly is measured 9 times with the instrument, calculate, to 3 decimal places, the probability that the mean of the 9 readings will be within 0.5 mm of the true length.   **(3 marks)**

    c Given that the mean of the 9 readings was 22.53 mm, determine a 98% confidence interval for the true body length of the butterfly.   **(3 marks)**

Chapter review (3)

(E) **1** The masses of bags of lentils, X kg, have a normal distribution with unknown mean μ kg and a known standard deviation σ kg. A random sample of 80 bags of lentils gave a 90% confidence interval for μ of $(0.4533, 0.5227)$.

    a Without carrying out any further calculations, use this confidence interval to test whether $\mu = 0.48$. State your hypotheses clearly and write down the **significance level** you have used.   **(3 marks)**

    A second random sample of 120 of these bags of lentils had a mean mass of 0.482 kg.

    b Calculate a 95% confidence interval for μ based on this second sample.   **(6 marks)**

(E/P) **2** The lengths of the tails of mice in a pet shop are assumed to have unknown mean μ and unknown standard deviation σ.

A random sample of 20 mice is taken and the length of their tails recorded.

The sample is represented by $X_1, X_2, \ldots, X_{20}$.

    a State whether or not the following are statistics.

    Give reasons for your answers.

    i $\dfrac{2X_1 + X_{20}}{3}$ **ii** $\displaystyle\sum_{1}^{20}(X_i - \mu)^2$ **iii** $\dfrac{\displaystyle\sum_{1}^{20}X_i^2}{n}$ **(4 marks)**

    b Find the mean and variance of $\dfrac{4X_1 - X_{20}}{3}$ **(3 marks)**

(E) **3** The breaking stresses of elastic bands are normally distributed.

A company uses bands with a mean breaking stress of 46.50 N.

A new supplier claims that they can supply bands that are stronger, and provides a sample of 100 bands for the company to test. The company checked the breaking stress X for each of these 100 bands and the results are summarised as follows:

$$n = 100 \qquad \sum x = 4715 \qquad \sum x^2 = 222\,910$$

    a Find an **approximate** 95% confidence interval for the mean breaking stress of these new rubber bands.   **(3 marks)**

    b Do you agree with the new supplier, that they can supply bands that are stronger?   **(2 marks)**

(E/P) **4** On each of 100 days, a scientist took a sample of 1 litre of water from a particular place along a river, and measured the amount, X mg, of chlorine in the sample. The results she obtained are shown in the table.

X	1	2	3	4	5	6	7	8	9
Number of days	4	8	20	22	16	13	10	6	1

    a Estimate the mean amount of chlorine present per litre of water, and estimate, to 3 decimal places, the standard error of this estimate.   **(3 marks)**

    b Obtain approximate 98% confidence limits for the mean amount of chlorine present per litre of water.   **(3 marks)**

    Given that measurements at the same point under the same conditions are taken for a further 100 days,

    c estimate, to 3 decimal places, the probability that the mean of these measurements will be greater than 4.6 mg per litre of water.   **(3 marks)**

(E) **5** The amount, to the nearest mg, of a certain chemical in particles in the air at a weather station was measured each day for 300 days. The results are shown in the table.

Amount of chemical (mg)	12	13	14	15	16
Number of days	5	42	210	31	12

    Estimate the mean amount of this chemical in the air, and find, to 2 decimal places, the standard error of this estimate.   **(3 marks)**

(E/P) **6** Occasionally, a firm manufacturing furniture needs to check the mean distance between pairs of holes drilled by a machine in pieces of wood to ensure that no change has occurred. It is known from experience that the standard deviation of the distance is 0.43 mm. The firm intends to take a random sample of size n, and to calculate a 99% confidence interval for the mean of the population. The width of this interval must be no more than 0.60 mm.

Calculate the minimum value of n.   **(4 marks)**

(E) **7** The times taken by five-year-old children to complete a certain task are normally distributed with a standard deviation of 8.0 s. In a random sample, 25 five-year-old children from school A were given this task and their mean time was 44.2 s.

    a Find 95% confidence limits for the mean time taken by five-year-old children from school A to complete this task.   **(3 marks)**

The mean time for a random sample of 20 five-year-old children from school B was 40.9 s. The headteacher of school B concluded that the overall mean for school B must be less than that of school A. Given that the two samples were independent,

b test the headteacher's conclusion using a 5% significance level. State your hypotheses clearly.

(6 marks)

E/P **8** The random variable X is normally distributed with mean μ and variance σ^2.

a Write down the distribution of the sample mean $\overline{X}$ of a random sample of size n. **(1 mark)**

b State, with a reason, whether this distribution is exact or is an estimate. **(1 mark)**

An efficiency expert wishes to determine the mean time taken to drill a fixed number of holes in a metal sheet.

c Determine how large a random sample is needed so that the expert can be 95% certain that the sample mean time will differ from the true mean time by less than 15 seconds. Assume that it is known from previous studies that $\sigma = 40$ seconds. **(4 marks)**

E/P **9** A man regularly uses a train service which should arrive in Zurich at 09:31. He decided to test this stated arrival time. Each weekday for a period of 4 weeks, he recorded the number of minutes X that the train was late on arrival in Zurich. If the train arrived early then the value of X was negative. His results are summarised as follows:

$$n = 20 \qquad \sum x = 15.0 \qquad \sum x^2 = 103.21$$

a Calculate unbiased estimates of the mean and variance of the number of minutes late of this train service. **(3 marks)**

The random variable X represents the number of minutes that the train is late on arriving in Zurich. Records kept by the railway company show that over fairly short periods, the standard deviation of X is 2.5 minutes. The man made two assumptions about the distribution of X and the values obtained in the sample and went on to calculate a 95% confidence interval for the mean arrival time of this train service.

b State the two assumptions. **(2 marks)**

c Find the confidence interval. **(3 marks)**

d Given that the assumptions are reasonable, comment on the stated arrival time of the service. **(1 mark)**

E/P **10** The random variable X is normally distributed with mean μ and variance σ^2.

a Write down the distribution of the sample mean $\overline{X}$ of a random sample of size n. **(1 mark)**

b Explain what you understand by a 95% confidence interval. **(2 marks)**

A garage sells both leaded and unleaded fuel. The distribution of the values of sales for each type is normal. During 2010, the standard deviation of individual sales of each type of fuel was £3.25. The mean of the individual sales of leaded fuel during this time was £8.72. A random sample of 100 individual sales of unleaded fuel gave a mean of £9.71.

Calculate:

c an interval within which 90% of the sales of leaded fuel will lie **(3 marks)**

d a 95% confidence interval for the mean sales of unleaded fuel. **(3 marks)**

The mean of the sales of unleaded fuel for 2009 was £9.10.

e Using a 5% significance level, investigate whether there is sufficient evidence to conclude that the mean of all the 2010 unleaded sales was greater than the mean of the 2009 sales.

(6 marks)

f Find the size of the sample that should be taken so that the garage owner can be 95% certain that the sample mean of sales of unleaded fuel during 2010 will differ from the true mean by less than £0.50.

(4 marks)

(E/P) **11 a** Explain what is meant by a 98% confidence interval for a population mean. **(2 marks)**

The lengths, in cm, of the leaves of oak trees are known to be normally distributed with variance 1.33 cm².

A sample of 40 oak tree leaves is found to have a mean of 10.20 cm.

b Estimate, giving your answer to 3 decimal places, the standard error of the mean. **(2 marks)**

c Use this value to estimate 95% confidence limits for the mean length of the population of oak tree leaves, giving your answer to 2 decimal places. **(3 marks)**

d Find the minimum size of the sample of leaves which must be taken if the width of the 98% confidence interval for the population mean is at most 1.50 cm. **(4 marks)**

(E/P) **12 a** Write down the mean and the variance of the distribution of the means of all possible samples of size n taken from an infinite population having mean μ and variance σ^2. **(2 marks)**

b Describe the form of this distribution of sample means when:

i n is large

ii the distribution of the population is normal. **(2 marks)**

The standard deviation of all the till receipts of a supermarket during 2014 was £4.25.

c Given that the mean of a random sample of 100 of the till receipts is £18.50, obtain an approximate 95% confidence interval for the mean of all the till receipts during 2014.

(3 marks)

d Find the size of sample that should be taken so that the management can be 95% confident that the sample mean will not differ from the true mean by more than £0.50. **(3 marks)**

e The mean of all the till receipts of the supermarket during 2013 was £19.40. Using a 5% significance level, investigate whether the sample in part **a** provides sufficient evidence to conclude that the mean of all the 2014 till receipts is different from that in 2013. **(6 marks)**

(E/P) **13** Records of the diameters of spherical metal balls produced on a certain machine show that the diameters are normally distributed with mean 0.824 cm and standard deviation 0.046 cm. Two hundred samples are randomly chosen, each consisting of 100 metal balls.

a Calculate the expected number of the 200 samples having a mean diameter less than 0.823 cm. **(2 marks)**

On a certain day, it was believed that the machine was faulty. It may be assumed that if the machine is faulty, it will change the mean of the diameters without changing their standard deviation. On that day, a random sample of 100 metal balls had mean diameter 0.834 cm.

b Determine a 98% confidence interval for the mean diameter of the metal balls being produced that day. **(3 marks)**

c Hence state whether or not you would conclude that the machine is faulty on that day given that the significance level is 2%. **(3 marks)**

(E/P) **14** A doctor claims that there is a higher mean heart rate in people who always drive to work compared to people who regularly walk to work. She measures the heart rates X of 30 people who always drive to work and 36 people who regularly walk to work. Her results are summarised in the table below.

	n	$\overline{x}$	s^2
Drive to work	30	52	60.2
Walk to work	36	47	55.8

   a Test, at the 5% level of significance, the doctor's claim. State your hypotheses clearly.

                                                                              (6 marks)

   b State any assumptions you have made in testing the doctor's claim.　　　**(2 marks)**

   The doctor decides to add another person who drives to work to her data.
   She measures the person's heart rate and finds $X = 55$.

   c Find an unbiased estimate of the variance for the sample of 31 people who drive to work. Give your answer to 3 significant figures.　　　**(4 marks)**

Challenge

SKILLS

ADAPTIVE LEARNING

Two independent random samples $X_1, X_2, \ldots, X_n$ and $Y_1, Y_2, \ldots, Y_m$ are taken from a population with mean μ and variance σ^2. The unbiased estimators $\overline{X}$ and $\overline{Y}$ of μ are calculated. A new unbiased estimator T of μ is sought in the form $T = r\overline{X} + s\overline{Y}$.

a Show that, since T is unbiased, $r + s = 1$.

b By writing $T = r\overline{X} + (1 - r)\overline{Y}$, show that:

$$\text{Var}(T) = \left(\sigma^2 \frac{r^2}{n} + \frac{1 - r^2}{m} \right)$$

c Show that the minimum variance of T is when $r = \dfrac{n}{n + m}$

d Find the best (in the sense of minimum variance) unbiased estimator of μ in the form $r\overline{X} + s\overline{Y}$.

Summary of key points

1 If X is a random variable, then a random sample of size n will consist of n observations of the random variable X, which are referred to as $X_1, X_2, X_3, \ldots, X_n$, where the X_i:

  • are independent random variables

  • each have the same distribution as X.

A statistic T is defined as a random variable consisting of any function of the X_i that involves no other quantities, such as unknown population parameters.

2 The **sampling distribution** of a statistic T is the probability distribution of T.

3 A statistic that is used to estimate a population parameter is called an **estimator** and the particular value of the estimator generated from the sample taken is called an **estimate**.

4 If a statistic T is used as an estimator for a population parameter θ and $E(T) = \theta$, then T is an unbiased estimator for θ.

5 If a statistic T is used as an estimator for a population parameter θ, then the bias is $E(T) - \theta$. For an unbiased estimator, the bias is 0.

6 An unbiased estimator for σ^2 is given by the **sample variance** S^2 where:

$$S^2 = \frac{1}{n-1} \sum_{i=1}^{n} (X_i - \overline{X})^2$$

7 The standard deviation of an estimator is called the **standard error** of the estimator.

8 When using the sample mean $\overline{X}$, you can use the following result for the standard error:

Standard error of $\overline{X} = \dfrac{\sigma}{\sqrt{n}}$ or $\dfrac{s}{\sqrt{n}}$

9 A **confidence interval** for a population parameter θ is a range of values defined so that there is a specific probability that the true value of the parameter lies within that range.

10 A 95% confidence interval for the population mean μ is $\left(\overline{x} - 1.96 \times \dfrac{\sigma}{\sqrt{n}}, \overline{x} + 1.96 \times \dfrac{\sigma}{\sqrt{n}} \right)$

11 The width of a confidence interval is the difference between the upper confidence limit and the lower confidence limit. This is $2 \times z \times \dfrac{\sigma}{\sqrt{n}}$, where z is the relevant percentage point from the standard normal distribution, for example 1.96, 1.6449, etc.

Review exercise

1

(E) **1** A researcher is hired by a cleaning company to survey the opinions of employees on a proposed pension scheme. The company employs 55 managers and 495 cleaners.

   a Explain what is meant by a census and give one disadvantage of using it in this context. **(2)**

To collect data, the researcher decides to give a questionnaire to the first 50 cleaners to leave at the end of the day.

   b State the sampling method used by the researcher. **(1)**

   c Give two reasons why this method is likely to produce biased results. **(2)**

   d Explain briefly how the researcher could select a sample of 50 employees using:

     i a systematic sample

     ii a stratified sample. **(2)**

     ← **Statistics 3 Sections 1.1, 1.2, 1.3**

2 Describe one advantage and one disadvantage of:

   a quota sampling

   b simple random sampling

     ← **Statistics 3 Sections 1.1, 1.4**

3 Mrs Hilyard wants to select a sample of 50 of her students to fill in a questionnaire. The school has a record of all 500 students, listed alphabetically and numbered 1 to 500.

Mrs Hilyard uses the same random number table that appears on page 144 of this textbook.

Starting with the top–left hand corner and working across, Mrs Hilyard chooses three random numbers. The first two suitable numbers are 384 and 100.

   a What are the next two suitable numbers?

Mrs Hilyard decides to take a systematic sample instead, using the same list.

   b Explain why a systematic sample may not give a sample that represents the proportion of boys and girls in the school.

   c Which sampling technique should Mrs Hilyard use?

     ← **Statistics 3 Sections 1.1, 1.2, 1.3**

4 A hotel has 320 rooms, of which 180 are classified as standard, 100 are classified as premier, and 40 are classified as executive.

The manager wants to obtain information about room usage in the hotel by taking a 10% sample of the rooms.

Explain how the manager should obtain a stratified sample.

     ← **Statistics 3 Section 1.2**

(E/P) **5** At an amusement park, the duration R seconds of a ride on the rollercoaster has the normal distribution $N(82, 3^2)$. The duration F of a ride on the Ferris Wheel has the normal distribution $N(238, 7^2)$. Alice rides on the rollercoaster and the Ferris Wheel.

   a Find the probability that her ride on the Ferris Wheel is less than three times as long as her ride on the rollercoaster. **(6)**

   b State one assumption you have made and comment on its validity. **(1)**

Paul rides on the rollercoaster three times in a row. The random variable D represents the total duration of the three rides.

   c Find the distribution of D. **(3)**

Given that Alice starts a ride on the Ferris Wheel at the same time as Paul starts his three rides on the rollercoaster,

d find the probability that Alice and Paul's rides finish within 10 seconds of one another. **(5)**

← Statistics 3 Section 2.1

E **6** A workshop makes two types of electrical resistor.

The resistance, X ohms, of resistors of Type A is such that $X \sim N(20, 4)$.

The resistance, Y ohms, of resistors of Type B is such that $Y \sim N(10, 0.84)$.

When a resistor of each type is connected into a circuit, the resistance R ohms of the circuit is given by $R = X + Y$, where X and Y are independent.

Find:

a $E(R)$ **(2)**

b $Var(R)$ **(2)**

c $P(28.90 < R < 32.64)$ **(3)**

← Statistics 3 Section 2.1

7 A simple random sample X_1, X_2, X_3 is taken from a normal distribution with mean μ and standard deviation σ.

Given that $\overline{X} = \dfrac{X_1 + X_2 + X_3}{3}$

and that $P\left(\dfrac{X_1 + X_2}{2} > \overline{X} + k\sigma\right) = 0.2$

where k is a contant, find the value of k, giving your answer correct to 3 s.f.

← Statistics 3 Section 2.1

8 In a bag, there are five coins worth 1 RMB, three coins worth 0.5 RMB and two coins worth 0.1 RMB. Two coins are taken from the bag without replacement and the mean value calculated.

Write down the sample distribution for the mean value.

← Statistics 3 Section 3.1

9 The random variable C is defined as:

$C = 2A + 5B$

where $A \sim N(15, 1.5^2)$ and $B \sim N(\mu, 2^2)$ and A and B are independent.

Given that $P(C < 83.5) = 0.9$, find the value of μ, giving your answer to 2 decimal places.

← Statistics 3 Section 2.1

E **10** The random variables A_1, A_2, A_3 and A_4 each have the same distribution as A, where $A \sim N(24, 4^2)$. The random variable X has distribution $X \sim N(20, 3^2)$.

The random variable B is defined as

$$B = 3X + \sum_{i=1}^{4} A_i$$

where X, A_1, A_2, A_3 and A_4 are independent. Find $P(B \leqslant 170 \,|\, B > 156)$

← Statistics 3 Section 2.1

11 The random variable X has a continuous uniform distribution over the interval $[\alpha - 3, 5\alpha - 9]$, where α is a constant.

The mean of a random sample of size n taken from this distribution is $\overline{X}$.

a Show that $\overline{X}$ is a biased estimator for α and calculate the bias of $\overline{X}$ when used as an estimator for α.

b Given that $Y = k\overline{X} + 4$ is an unbiased estimator, find the value of k.

A random sample of 10 values of X is taken and the results are as follows:

     17   42.5   32.2   42.3   46

     45   46.3   30.7   11.7   49.9

c Use the sample to estimate the maximum value that X can take.

← Statistics 3 Sections 3.1, 3.2

E **12** The weights of adult men are normally distributed with a mean of 84 kg and a standard deviation of 11 kg.

a Find the probability that the total weight of 4 randomly chosen adult men is less than 350 kg. **(3)**

The weights of adult women are normally distributed with a mean of 62 kg and a standard deviation of 10 kg.

b Find the probability that the weight of a randomly chosen adult man is less than one and a half times the weight of a randomly chosen adult woman. **(4)**

← **Statistics 3 Section 3.1**

E **13** The random variable D is defined as
$$D = A - 3B + 4C$$
where $A \sim N(5, 2^2)$, $B \sim N(7, 3^2)$ and $C \sim N(9, 4^2)$, and A, B and C are independent.

a Find $P(D < 44)$ **(4)**

The random variables B_1, B_2 and B_3 are independent and each has the same distribution as B.

The random variable X is defined as
$$X = A - \sum_{i=1}^{3} B_i + 4C$$

b Find $P(X > 0)$ **(4)**

← **Statistics 3 Section 2.1**

E **14** A manufacturer produces two flavours of soft drink: cola and lemonade. The weights, C and L, in grams, of randomly selected cola and lemonade cans are such that $C \sim N(350, 8)$ and $L \sim N(345, 17)$.

a Find the probability that the weights of two randomly selected cans of cola will differ by more than 6 g. **(4)**

One can of each flavour is selected at random.

b Find the probability that the can of cola weighs more than the can of lemonade. **(3)**

Cans are delivered to shops in boxes of 24 cans. The weights of empty boxes are normally distributed with mean 100 g and standard deviation 2 g.

c Find the probability that a full box of cola cans weighs between 8.51 kg and 8.52 kg. **(4)**

d State an assumption you made in your calculation in part **c**. **(1)**

← **Statistics 3 Section 3.1**

E/P **15** In a trial of diet A, a random sample of 80 participants was taken to record their weight loss, x kg, after their first week of using the diet. The results are summarised as follows:
$$\sum x = 361.6 \qquad \sum x^2 = 1753.95$$

a Find unbiased estimates for the mean and variance of weight lost after the first week of using diet A. **(3)**

The designers of diet A believe it can achieve a greater mean weight loss after the first week than an existing diet B.

A random sample of 60 people used diet B. After the first week they had achieved a mean weight loss of 4.06 kg, with an unbiased estimate of variance of weight loss of 2.50 kg^2.

b Test, at the 5% level of significance, whether or not the mean weight loss after the first week using diet A is greater than that using diet B. State your hypotheses clearly. **(6)**

c Explain the significance of the central limit theorem to the test in part **b**. **(1)**

d State an assumption you have made in carrying out the test in part **b**. **(1)**

← **Statistics 3 Sections 3.1, 3.4**

E/P **16** A random sample of the daily sales (in Rand) of a small company is taken and, using tables of the normal distribution, a 99% confidence interval for the mean daily sales is found to be (123.5, 154.7).

Find a 95% confidence interval for the mean daily sales of the company. **(6)**

← **Statistics 3 Section 3.2**

(E) **17** A machine produces metal containers. The masses of the containers are normally distributed. A random sample of 10 containers was taken and the mass of each container was recorded to the nearest 0.1 kg. The results were as follows:

49.7	50.3	51.0	49.5	49.9
50.1	50.2	50.0	49.6	49.7

  a Find unbiased estimates of the mean and variance of the masses of the population of metal containers. **(3)**

The machine is set to produce metal containers whose masses have a population standard deviation of 0.5 kg.

  b For the population mean, find:

    i a 95% confidence interval

    ii a 99% confidence interval **(5)**

← **Statistics 3 Sections 3.1, 3.2**

(E/P) **18** The drying times of paint can be assumed to be normally distributed. A paint manufacturer paints 10 test areas with a new paint. The following drying times, to the nearest minute, were recorded:

82	98	140	110	90
125	150	130	70	110

  a Calculate unbiased estimates for the mean and the variance of the population of drying times of this paint. **(3)**

Given that the population standard deviation is 25,

  b find a 95% confidence interval for the mean drying time of this paint. **(5)**

Fifteen similar sets of tests are done and the 95% confidence interval is determined for each set.

  c Find the probability that all 15 of these confidence intervals contain the population mean. **(2)**

← **Statistics 3 Sections 3.1, 3.2**

(E) **19** Some biologists were studying a large group of birds. A random sample of 36 were measured and the wing length, x mm, of each bird was recorded. The results are summarised as follows:

$$\sum x = 6046 \qquad \sum x^2 = 1\,016\,338$$

  a Calculate unbiased estimates for the mean and the variance of the wing lengths of these birds. **(3)**

Given that the wing lengths are assumed to be normally distributed and that the standard deviation of the wing lengths of this particular type of bird is actually 5.1 mm,

  b find a 99% confidence interval for the mean wing length of the birds from this group. **(3)**

← **Statistics 3 Sections 3.1, 3.2**

(E/P) **20** A computer company repairs large numbers of PCs and wants to estimate the mean time taken to repair a particular fault. Five repairs are chosen at random from the company's records and the times taken, in seconds, are as follows:

205	310	405	195	320

  a Calculate unbiased estimates of the mean and the variance of the population of repair times from which this sample has been taken. **(3)**

It is known from previous results that the standard deviation of the repair time for this fault is 100 seconds and that the repair time is normally distributed. The company manager wants to ensure that there is a probability of at least 0.95 that the estimate of the population mean lies within 20 seconds of its true value.

  b Find the minimum sample size required. **(5)**

← **Statistics 3 Sections 3.1, 3.2**

21 A company makes individual slices of cheesecake. The weight of each slice is normally distributed with mean 135 g and standard deviation 3 g.

It is possible to buy a box of 12 individual slices of cheesecake. The box has a weight which is normally distributed with weight 100 g and standard deviation 6 g.

  a Find the probability that the weight of the 12 slices and the box is greater than 1.7 kg.

  b What assumptions about the weights of the slices of cheesecake are you making?

  ← **Statistics 3 Sections 3.1, 3.2**

22 Maike found a 95% confidence interval to be (14.6904, 15.7096)

Unfortunately, he had lost his original information, but he did remember that the standard deviation was 1.3

Calculate the sample size that Maike used to create this confidence interval.

  ← **Statistics 3 Section 3.2**

23 A $c\%$ confidence interval was calculated using 36 observations from a data set which is normally distributed. The value of s was 3.6

The confidence interval calculated was (12.9636, 16.2364).

  a Find the value of $\bar{x}$.

  b Find the value of c.

  ← **Statistics 3 Section 3.2**

SKILLS   INNOVATION

Challenge

A random sample of three independent variables X_1, X_2 and X_3 is taken from a distribution with mean μ and variance σ^2.

  a Show that $\frac{2}{3}X_1 - \frac{1}{2}X_2 + \frac{5}{6}X_3$ is an unbiased estimator for μ.

An unbiased estimator for μ is given by $\hat{\mu} = aX_1 + bX_2$ where a and b are **constants**.

  b Show that $\text{Var}(\hat{\mu}) = (2a^2 - 2a + 1)\sigma^2$.

  c Hence determine the value of a and the value of b for which $\hat{\mu}$ has minimum variance.

  ← **Statistics 3 Section 3.1**

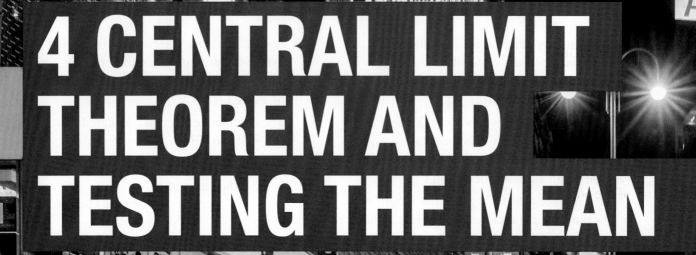

4 CENTRAL LIMIT THEOREM AND TESTING THE MEAN

Learning objectives

After completing this chapter you should be able to:

Prior knowledge check

1 A random variable $X \sim N(120, 8^2)$. Find:

  a $P(X > 115)$ **b** $P(120 < X < 130)$

  c a such that $P(X < a) = 0.25$

      ← **Statistics 1 Sections 7.1, 7.3**

2 A fair six-sided dice is rolled. Let X be the score on the uppermost face, and let $Y = 1 - 3X$. Find:

  a $E(Y)$ **b** $Var(Y)$

  c $P(Y < -5)$ ← **Statistics 3 Sections 6.5, 6.6**

3 Robin flips a fair coin until he gets five heads. Find the probability that the coin is flipped at least 12 times.   ← **Statistics 2 Section 2.2**

The central limit theorem gives information about the distribution of the **sample mean**, even when the distribution of the population is unknown. Statisticians use it to infer how likely the views of a sample are to be representative of the population.

→ **Chapter review 4 Q10**

4.1 The central limit theorem

If you take a random sample of n observations from a normally distributed random variable $X \sim N(\mu, \sigma^2)$, then the **sample mean** $\overline{X}$ is also normally distributed with $\overline{X} \sim N\left(\mu, \frac{\sigma^2}{n}\right)$.

In fact, this result is a special case of a more powerful result called the **central limit theorem**. This states that the mean of a large random sample taken from any random variable is always approximately normally distributed. This result is true without paying attention to the distribution of the original random variable.

- The central limit theorem says that if $X_1, X_2, \ldots, X_n$ is a random sample of size n from a population with mean μ and variance σ^2, then $\overline{X}$ is approximately $\sim N\left(\mu, \frac{\sigma^2}{n}\right)$.

In general, the sample mean is only **approximately** distributed with $N\left(\mu, \frac{\sigma^2}{n}\right)$. As n gets larger, this **approximation** gets better.

The variance of the sample mean also decreases as n gets large. You can say that for a large sample, the sample mean will be very close to the population mean.

Example 1

A six-sided dice is changed so that there are three faces marked 1, two faces marked 3 and one face marked 6. The dice is rolled 40 times and the mean of the 40 scores is recorded.

a Find an approximate distribution for the mean of the scores.

b Use your approximation to estimate the probability that the mean is greater than 3.

---

a Let the random variable X represent the score on a single roll.

Then the distribution of X is:

x	1	3	6
$P(X = x)$	$\frac{1}{2}$	$\frac{1}{3}$	$\frac{1}{6}$

So: $\mu = E(X) = \sum x P(X = x)$

$= 1 \times \frac{1}{2} + 3 \times \frac{1}{3} + 6 \times \frac{1}{6}$

$= 2.5$

and $\sigma^2 = Var(X)$

$= \sum x^2 P(X = x) - \mu^2$

$= 1^2 \times \frac{1}{2} + 3^2 \times \frac{1}{3} + 6^2 \times \frac{1}{6} - \left(\frac{5}{2}\right)^2$

$= \frac{19}{2} - \frac{25}{4} = 3.25$ or $\frac{13}{4}$

Now by the central limit theorem:

$\overline{X} \approx \sim N\left(2.5, \frac{13}{160}\right)$

> **Problem-solving**
>
> Find the mean and variance of the **discrete** distribution.   ← **Statistics 1 Sections 6.3, 6.4**

> The population is clearly not normally distributed but the sample size ($n = 40$) is quite large so the central limit theorem can be used.

b $P(\bar{X} > 3) = 1 - P\left(Z < \dfrac{3 - 2.5}{\sqrt{\dfrac{13}{160}}}\right)$

$= 1 - P(Z < 1.75...)$

$= 1 - 0.9599$

$= 0.0401$

Standardising and using tables

Watch out   You do not need to apply a **continuity correction** when using the central limit theorem. This is because the underlying distribution is the mean of the sample. Although this is a **discrete random variable**, it does not have to take integer values. It takes fractional values, and the gaps between values get smaller and smaller as n gets larger.

Exercise (**4A**)   **SKILLS**   ANALYSIS

(E/P)   **1**   The lengths of bolts produced by a machine have an unknown distribution with mean 3.03 cm and standard deviation 0.20 cm.

A sample of 100 bolts is taken.

a   Estimate the probability that the mean length of this sample is less than 3 cm.   **(3 marks)**

A second sample is taken. The probability that the mean of this sample is less than 3 cm needs to be less than 1%.

b   Find the minimum sample size required.   **(5 marks)**

(E)   **2**   A random variable X has the **discrete uniform distribution**

$$P(X = x) = \tfrac{1}{5} \qquad x = 1, 2, 3, 4, 5$$

40 observations are taken from X, and their mean $\bar{X}$ is recorded.

Find an estimate for $P(\bar{X} > 3.2)$ **(6 marks)**

(P)   **3**   A fair dice is rolled 35 times.

a   Find the approximate probability that the mean of the 35 scores is more than 4.

b   Find the approximate probability that the total of the 35 scores is less than 100.

4   The 25 children in a class each roll a fair dice 30 times and record the number of sixes they obtain. Find an estimate of the probability that the mean number of sixes recorded for the class is less than 4.5.

(E)   **5**   The random variable X has the probability distribution shown in the table.

x	0	2	3	5
$P(X = x)$	0.1	$3k$	k	0.3

a   Find the value of k.   **(2 marks)**

A random sample of 100 observations of X is taken.

b   Use the central limit theorem to estimate the probability that the mean of these observations is greater than 3.   **(6 marks)**

c   Comment on the accuracy of your estimate.   **(1 mark)**

(P) **6** A fair dice is rolled n times. Given that there is less than a 1% chance that the mean of all the scores differs from 3.5 by more than 0.1, find the minimum sample size.

(E/P) **7** The annual part-time salaries of employees at a large company have an unknown distribution with mean AUD\$28,500 and standard deviation AUD\$6800.

A random sample of 5 members of the senior management team is taken.

A researcher suggests that N$(28\,500, \frac{6800^2}{5})$ could be used to model the distribution of the sample mean.

a Give a reason why this is unlikely to be a good **model**. **(1 mark)**

A second random sample of 15 employees from the whole company is taken.

b Estimate the probability that the mean annual salary of these employees is:
  i less than AUD\$25,000 **ii** between AUD\$25,000 and AUD\$30,000. **(4 marks)**

c Comment on the accuracy of your estimate. **(1 mark)**

(E/P) **8** An electrical company repairs very large numbers of television sets and wishes to estimate the mean time taken to repair a particular fault. It is known from previous research that the standard deviation of the time taken to repair this particular fault is 2.5 minutes. The manager wishes to ensure that the probability that the estimate differs from the true mean by less than 30 seconds is 0.95.

Find how large a sample is required. **(6 marks)**

4.2 Applying the central limit theorem to other distributions

You can use the central limit theorem to solve problems involving other distributions such as the binomial, the Poisson and the uniform distributions.

Example 2

A supermarket manager is trying to model the number of customers who visit her store each day. She observes that, on average, 20 new customers enter the store every minute.

a Calculate the probability that fewer than 4 customers arrive in a given 15-second **interval**.

b Use the central limit theorem to estimate the probability that in one hour no more than 1150 customers arrive.

---

a Let X represent the number of customers who arrive in one minute.

Then $X \sim$ Po(20)

Let Y represent the number of customers who arrive in a 15-second interval.

Then $Y \sim$ Po(5)

P$(Y < 5) = 0.4405$, from tables

It's reasonable to assume that customers arrive independently of each other at a **constant** rate, so the number of customers arriving each minute will have a Poisson distribution.

← **Statistics 2 Section 2.2**

b Consider a sample of 60 observations taken from X.

By the central limit theorem, $\overline{X}$ is approximately $\sim N\left(20, \frac{20}{60}\right)$, or $N\left(20, \frac{1}{3}\right)$.

If $T \leqslant 1150$ then $\overline{X} \leqslant \frac{1150}{60} = 19.1666\ldots$

So $P(T \leqslant 1150) = P(\overline{X} \leqslant 19.1666\ldots)$

Standardising:

$P(\overline{X} \leqslant 19.1666\ldots) = P\left(Z \leqslant \dfrac{19.1666 - 20}{\frac{1}{\sqrt{3}}}\right)$

$= P(Z \leqslant -1.44\ldots)$

$= 1 - P(Z \leqslant 1.44\ldots)$

$= 1 - 0.9251$

$= 0.0749$

You could also consider the number of customers who arrive in one hour as a sample of 60 observations from X, the number who arrive in one minute.

Problem-solving

If $\sum X_i$ is the sum of the observations from a sample of size n, then the sample mean is given by:

$$\overline{X} = \frac{\sum X_i}{n}$$

From tables

Exercise (4B)

1 A random sample of 10 observations is taken from a Poisson distribution with mean 3.

  a Find the exact probability that the sample mean does not exceed 2.5.

  b Estimate the probability that the sample mean does not exceed 2.5 using the central limit theorem, and compare your answer to part **a**.

(E) **2** A sample of size 20 is taken from a binomial distribution with $n = 10$ and $p = 0.2$
Estimate the probability that the sample mean does not exceed 2.4   **(4 marks)**

(E/P) **3** There are 20 children in a class. Each flips a biased coin 15 times. The probability of getting a head is 0.25.

  a Write down the expected number of heads that each child would get.   **(2 marks)**

  b Find an estimate of the probability that the mean number of heads is at most 4.   **(3 marks)**

(E/P) **4** A town is hit by three thunderstorms per month, on average.

  a Find the probability that there are four thunderstorms next month.   **(2 marks)**

  b Use the central limit theorem to estimate the probability that over the course of a year, the average number of thunderstorms each month is at most 2.5   **(4 marks)**

5 The continuous random variable X is uniformly distributed over the interval

    $[a - 3, 3a + 5]$

where a is a constant.

40 observations of X will be taken.

Use the central limit theorem to find an approximate distribution for $\overline{X}$.

6 Telephone calls arrive at a call centre at an average rate of two per minute.
Over a period of 30 days, a telephone operator records the number of calls
each day that arrive in the five-minute period before her break.

    a Find an approximation for the probability that the total number of calls
recorded is more than 350.   **(2 marks)**

    b Estimate the probability that the mean number of calls received in this
period each day is less than 9.0.   **(4 marks)**

4.3 Confidence intervals using the central limit theorem

We can now state that, for large enough n, we can use the central limit theorem

to state that $\overline{X}$ approximately $\sim N\left(\mu, \dfrac{\sigma^2}{n}\right)$.

We can now find confidence intervals for μ.

Example 3   SKILLS   REASONING/ARGUMENTATION

A random sample of size 30 is taken from a population with standard deviation 2.2.
The mean of the sample is 18.3

a State the importance of the central limit theorem in finding a confidence interval for μ.

b Find a 90% C.I. for the population mean μ.

c What size sample is required to obtain a 90% C.I. with a width of at most 1?

---

a Since the population is not normally distributed
and n is large, we can use the central limit
theorem to approximate the sample mean as a
normal distribution.

b 90% confidence limits are:
$$\bar{x} \pm 1.6449 \times \frac{a}{\sqrt{n}} = 18.3 + 1.6449 \times \frac{2.2}{\sqrt{30}}$$

So a 90% confidence interval is (17.64, 18.96)

c Width of 90% C.I. is $2 \times 1.6449 \times \dfrac{2.2}{\sqrt{n}}$

$$2 \times 1.6449 \times \frac{2.2}{\sqrt{n}} < 1$$
$$7.23756 < \sqrt{n}$$
$$52.38\ldots < n$$
$$n = 53$$

> **Hint**   Remember, the central limit theorem
> allows us to approximate – we do not need
> to make any assumptions about the original
> distribution. Also remember that it is the
> sample mean we are approximating.

> **Hint**   Use the table on page 136 to find the
> value 1.6449.
> Make sure that you use the full value and
> you do not round it.

> **Hint**   The width is at most 1

Exercise 4C   SKILLS   REASONING/ARGUMENTATION

1 An investigation was carried out into the total distance travelled by vans in current use.
The standard deviation can be assumed to be 15000 km. In a random sample, 80 vans
were stopped and their mean distance travelled was found to be 7587 km.

    a Find a 90% confidence interval for the mean distance travelled by vans in current use.

    b State the importance of the central limit theorem.

2 The number of hours for which an electronic device can retain its information has a uniform distribution over the range $[\mu - 10, \mu + 10]$

a Show that the variance of the number of hours that the device can retain its information is $\dfrac{100}{3}$.

A random sample of 120 devices was tested and the mean number of hours they retained their information for was 78.7

b Find a 95% confidence interval for μ.

c What is the relevance of the central limit theorem in finding this confidence interval?

3 The mean value of T-shirts sold to a random sample of 40 standard ticket holders at a concert is 175RMB with a standard deviation of 80RMB.

a Calculate a 95% confidence interval for the mean value of T-shirts sold.

b State whether or not it is necessary to assume that the value of merchandise sold has a normal distribution. Give a reason for your answer.

4 A supermarket states that a carton of ice cream contain 15% fat.

Maike takes a random sample of 50 cartons from the supermarket and finds that they contain a mean fat content of 14.5% with a standard deviation of 1.5%.

a Find the 90% confidence interval for the mean fat content of a carton of ice cream from the supermarket.

b State, with a reason, what action Maike should recommend the supermarket takes regarding the stated fat content of their cartons of ice cream.

5 A chicken farmer knows that the mean mass μ kg for a large population of chickens will vary from season to season but the standard deviation of the masses should remain at 0.70 kg. A random sample of 100 chickens is taken from the population and the mass X kg of each chicken in the sample is recorded, giving $\Sigma x = 190.2$

a State with a reason, whether or not the central limit theorem will be used to find a confidence interval.

b Find a 95% confidence interval for μ.

6 The **continuous random variable** Y is **uniformly** distributed over the interval $[a - 4, a + 8]$ where a is a constant. A random sample of 30 observations of Y is taken.

Given that $\overline{Y} = \dfrac{\displaystyle\sum_{i=1}^{30} Y_i}{30}$

a use the central limit theorem to find an approximate distribution for $\overline{Y}$.

b Given that the 30 observations of Y have a sample mean of 12.6, find a 99% confidence interval for the maximum value that Y can take.

4.4 Hypothesis testing the mean

In the Statistics 2 book, you met the idea of a hypothesis test and a definition of it is given below.

- A hypothesis test about a population parameter θ tests a **null hypothesis** H_0, specifying a particular value for θ against an **alternative hypothesis** H_1, which will indicate whether the test is one-tailed or two-tailed.

The parameters considered were the proportion p of a binomial distribution and the mean λ or μ of a Poisson distribution. In this section you will learn how to extend the idea to test for μ, the mean, of a normal distribution. The process is similar to that of a trial in a courtroom. The null hypothesis is on trial, evidence is presented and the jury has to make a decision 'on the balance of probability'.

Example **4**   **SKILLS**   REASONING/ARGUMENTATION; INTERPRETATION

A certain company sells fruit juice in cartons. The amount of juice in a carton has a normal distribution with a standard deviation of 3 ml.

The company claims that the mean amount of juice per carton μ is 60 ml. A trading inspector has received complaints that the company is overstating the mean amount of juice per carton and he wishes to investigate this complaint. The trading inspector took a random sample of 16 cartons which gave a mean of 59.1 ml.

Using a 5% level of significance, and stating your hypotheses clearly, test whether or not there is evidence to justify this complaint.

The hypotheses are:

$H_0: \mu = 60$ $H_1: \mu < 60$

This is like the 'evidence' presented at a trial.
The sample gives $n = 16$ and $\bar{x} = 59.1$

$$P(\overline{X} \leqslant 59.1 | \mu = 60) = P\left(Z \leqslant \dfrac{59.1 - 60}{\frac{3}{4}}\right)$$

$$= P(Z \leqslant -1.2)$$

$$= 0.1151$$

$0.1151 > 0.05$ so the result is not significant and there is insufficient evidence to reject H_0, that $\mu = 60$.

The conclusion should incorporate two statements:
1 State whether or not the test is significant.
2 Interpret this in the context of the question.

There is insufficient evidence to support the complaint.

Remember, H_0 must specify a particular value of μ. The inspector therefore will assume that the company is innocent and wants to formulate a null hypothesis to express this idea in terms of the parameter μ.

If the company is guilty then μ must be less than 60 (there would be few complaints if the cartons contained on average more than 60 ml) and so the alternative hypothesis is $H_1: \mu < 60$. This means the test is one-tailed.

The inspector (like the jury in a trial) then has to calculate the probability of obtaining evidence 'as bad or worse' than this, assuming that the null hypothesis is true.

The alternative hypothesis is that the company is deceiving customers and that $\mu < 60$; the inspector's sample gave a mean of 59.1 and so any value of the sample mean less than or equal to 59.1 will be 'as bad or worse'.

You know that $\overline{X} \sim N\left(\mu, \dfrac{\sigma^2}{n}\right)$ so standardise to use the tables.

This probability is greater than the 5% significance level so there is no reason to suspect the validity of H_0.

Note that the test was based on the statistic

$$Z = \frac{\overline{X} - 60}{\frac{3}{\sqrt{n}}}$$

and this is the **test statistic** in this case.

> **Hint**   Recall that a statistic must not contain any unknown population parameters.

- The test statistic in a test for the population mean μ is $Z = \dfrac{\overline{X} - \mu}{\frac{\sigma}{\sqrt{n}}}$ where μ is the value given by the null hypothesis and σ is given.

It is sometimes helpful to consider what value z of the test statistic the inspector in Example 4 would have needed if he were to reject the hypothesis that $\mu = 60$. If you use a 5% significance level then:

$$P(Z \leqslant -1.6449) = 0.05$$

so any value of $z \leqslant -1.6449$ would mean that the probability of obtaining a sample 'as bad or worse' is less than or equal to 5%, which is unlikely. This means that the assumption that H_0 is true is called into question and we reject H_0 at the 5% level of significance.

> **Notation**   A significant result is one where the null hypothesis is rejected. This is like a guilty verdict in a trial. The judge concludes that the probability of the defendant being innocent and evidence 'as bad or worse' as that presented is so small as to make it improbable that the assumption of innocence is sustainable.

We call the region $Z \leqslant -1.6449$ the **critical region** of the statistic Z and the value -1.6449 is sometimes called the **critical value**.

- The critical region of a test statistic T is the range of values of T such that if the value of T, namely t, obtained from your particular sample lies in this critical region then you reject the null hypothesis.
- The boundary value(s) of the critical region is (are) called the critical value(s).

In tests for μ, the mean of a normal distribution are best carried out using the test statistic z and the critical region rather than calculating the probability.

> **Notation**   Note that in this case the critical values can be found so that the probability of lying in the critical region equals the significance level. In the Statistics 2 book we were applying these ideas to discrete distributions and an exact match was usually not possible. The continuous nature of the normal distribution enables us to achieve this here.

Example **5**   **SKILLS**   REASONING/ARGUMENTATION

At a certain college, new students are weighed when they join the college. The distribution of weights of students at the college when they enrol has a standard deviation of 7.5 kg and a mean of 70 kg. A random sample of 90 students from the new entry were weighed and their mean weight was 71.6 kg. Assuming that the standard deviation has not changed:

> **Notation**   Note that the question does not say that the weights are normally distributed. You will have to invoke the central limit theorem here and that is the reason for part **b**.

a test, at the 5% level, whether there is evidence that the mean of the new entry is more than 70 kg.

b State the importance of the central limit theorem to your test.

a $H_0: \mu = 70$ $H_1: \mu > 70$

$\sigma = 7.5$

A 5% significance level is required so the critical region for Z will be as shown by the diagram on the right.

From the table on page 136 this is

$Z \geqslant 1.6449$.

The sample gives $n = 90$, $\bar{x} = 71.6$ and these give a value of the test

statistic of $z = \dfrac{71.6 - 70}{\dfrac{7.5}{\sqrt{90}}} = 2.0239$

f(z)

0.05

Z

This value is in the critical region, so you reject H_0 and conclude that there is evidence that the new class have a higher mean weight.

Hint Always give a conclusion in context.

b The central limit theorem is used to assume that $\overline{X}$ (which is the mean weight of the 90 students) is normally distributed.

Example 6   **SKILLS**   REASONING/ARGUMENTATION

A machine produces bolts of diameter D, where D has a normal distribution with mean 0.580 cm and standard deviation 0.015 cm.

The machine is serviced, and after the service a random sample of 50 bolts from the next production run is taken to see if the mean diameter of the bolts has changed from 0.580 cm. The distribution of the diameters of bolts after the service is still normal with a standard deviation of 0.015 cm. The mean diameter of the 50 bolts is 0.577 cm.

a Stating your hypotheses clearly test, at the 1% level, whether or not there is evidence that the mean diameter of the bolts has changed.

b Find the critical region for $\overline{X}$ in the above test.

---

a $H_0: \mu = 0.580$ $H_1: \mu \neq 0.580$

$\sigma = 0.015$

A 1% significance test is required, so the critical region for Z will be as shown by the diagram on the right.

From the table on page 136 the critical region of Z is:

$Z \leqslant -2.5758$ or $Z \geqslant 2.5758$

The sample gives $n = 50$, $\bar{x} = 0.577$ so the value of the test statistic is:

$z = \dfrac{0.577 - 0.580}{\dfrac{0.015}{\sqrt{50}}} = 1.414...$

The word 'changed' in the question suggests that the alternative hypothesis is $\mu \neq 0.580$, so a two-tailed test is needed.

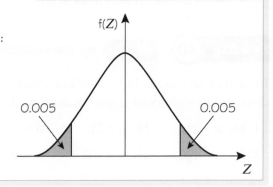

f(Z)

0.005   0.005

Z

This is not in the critical region so you accept H_0 and conclude that there is no significant evidence that the mean diameter has changed.

b The critical region of Z is:

$$Z \leqslant -2.5758 \text{ or } Z \geqslant 2.5758$$

So $Z = \dfrac{\overline{X} - 0.580}{\frac{0.015}{\sqrt{50}}} \leqslant -2.5758$

i.e. $\overline{X} \leqslant 0.580 - 2.5758 \times \dfrac{0.015}{\sqrt{50}} = 0.5745\ldots$

or $Z = \dfrac{\overline{X} - 0.580}{\frac{0.015}{\sqrt{50}}} \geqslant 2.5758$

i.e. $\overline{X} \geqslant 0.580 + 2.5758 \times \dfrac{0.015}{\sqrt{50}} = 0.5854\ldots$

So the critical region for $\overline{X}$ is:

$$\overline{X} \leqslant 0.575 \text{ or } \overline{X} \geqslant 0.585$$

Note that $\overline{x} = 0.577$ does not lie in the critical region

Hint Always give your conclusion in context – mention 'mean diameter'.

Use the critical regions for Z and the $Z = \dfrac{\overline{X} - \mu}{\frac{\sigma}{\sqrt{n}}}$ formula to form critical regions for $\overline{X}$.

Notation Notice that there is a similarity between a confidence interval and the critical region for a two-tailed hypothesis test. In this example the critical region was $\overline{X} \leqslant 0.575$ or $\overline{X} \geqslant 0.585$ and found from calculating $\mu \pm 2.5758 \times \dfrac{\sigma}{\sqrt{n}}$ and taking the region outside.

The 99% confidence interval is simply $(0.572, 0.582)$ and found by calculating $\overline{x} + 2.5758 \times \dfrac{\sigma}{\sqrt{n}}$ and taking the region inside.

Notice that the critical region uses μ and the confidence interval uses $\overline{x}$.

The following four steps summarise the stages in answering questions about hypothesis tests for the mean μ.

1 Identify the sample mean $\overline{x}$ and value for the population mean given by the null hypothesis.

2 Write down the null (H_0) and alternative (H_1) hypotheses. The alternative hypothesis will determine whether you want a one-tailed or a two-tailed test.

3 Calculate the value of the test statistic $z = \dfrac{\overline{x} - \mu}{\frac{\sigma}{\sqrt{n}}}$

4 Either using the critical region for Z, or by calculating a probability, complete the test and state your conclusions. The following points should be addressed.

    a Is the result significant or not?

    b What are the implications in terms of the context of the original problem?

Exercise **4D**   **SKILLS**   REASONING/ARGUMENTATION

In each of Questions 1–5, a random sample of size n is taken from a population having a normal distribution with mean μ and variance σ^2. Test the hypotheses at the 5% level of significance.

1 H_0: $\mu = 21$, H_1: $\mu \neq 21$, $n = 20$, $\overline{x} = 21.2$, $\sigma = 1.5$

2 H_0: $\mu = 100$, H_1: $\mu < 100$, $n = 36$, $\overline{x} = 98.5$, $\sigma = 5.0$

3 $H_0: \mu = 5,$ $H_1: \mu \neq 5,$ $n = 25,$ $\bar{x} = 6.1,$ $\sigma = 3.0$

4 $H_0: \mu = 15,$ $H_1: \mu > 15,$ $n = 40,$ $\bar{x} = 16.5,$ $\sigma = 3.5$

5 $H_0: \mu = 50,$ $H_1: \mu \neq 50,$ $n = 60,$ $\bar{x} = 48.9,$ $\sigma = 4.0$

In each of Questions 6–10, a random sample of size n is taken from a population having a $\mathrm{N}(\mu, \sigma^2)$ distribution. Find the critical regions for the test statistic $\bar{X}$ in the following tests.

6 $H_0: \mu = 120,$ $H_1: \mu < 120,$ $n = 30,$ $\sigma = 2.0,$ at the 5% level

7 $H_0: \mu = 12.5,$ $H_1: \mu > 12.5,$ $n = 25,$ $\sigma = 1.5,$ at the 1% level

8 $H_0: \mu = 85,$ $H_1: \mu < 85,$ $n = 50,$ $\sigma = 4.0,$ at the 10% level

9 $H_0: \mu = 0,$ $H_1: \mu \neq 0,$ $n = 45,$ $\sigma = 3.0,$ at the 5% level

10 $H_0: \mu = -8,$ $H_1: \mu \neq -8,$ $n = 20,$ $\sigma = 1.2,$ at the 1% level

11 The times taken for a capful of stain remover to remove a standard chocolate stain from a baby's bib are normally distributed with a mean of 185 seconds and a standard deviation of 15 seconds. The manufacturers of the stain remover claim to have developed a new formula which will shorten the time taken for a stain to be removed. A random sample of 25 capfuls of the new formula are tested and the mean time for the sample is 179 seconds.

Test, at the 5% level, whether or not there is evidence that the new formula is an improvement.

12 The IQ scores of a population are normally distributed with mean 100 and standard deviation 15. A psychologist wants to test the theory that eating chocolate before sitting an IQ test improves your score. A random sample of 100 people are selected and they are each given a 100 g bar of chocolate to eat before taking a standard IQ test. Their mean score on the test was 102.5.

Test the psychologist's theory at the 5% level.

13 The diameters of circular cardboard drinks mats produced by a certain machine are normally distributed with a mean of 9 cm and a standard deviation of 0.15 cm. After the machine is serviced a random sample of 30 mats is selected and their diameters are measured to see if the mean diameter has altered.

The mean of the sample was 8.95 cm. Test, at the 5% level, whether there is significant evidence of a change in the mean diameter of mats produced by the machine.

4.5 Hypothesis testing for the difference between means

You need to be able to carry out a hypothesis test for the **difference** between the means of two normal distributions with known variances.

If, instead of one population, you now have two independent populations, then you can test hypotheses about the difference between the population means.

In Chapter 2 you saw that if X and Y are two independent normal distributions with means of μ_x and μ_y and standard deviations σ_x and σ_y respectively, then:

$$X - Y \sim \mathrm{N}(\mu_x - \mu_y, \sigma_x^2 + \sigma_y^2)$$

Now, if $\overline{X}$ and $\overline{Y}$ are sample means based on samples of size n_x and n_y respectively from the above two normal distributions, then:

$$\overline{X} - \overline{Y} \sim N\left(\mu_x - \mu_y, \frac{\sigma_x^2}{n_x} + \frac{\sigma_y^2}{n_y}\right)$$

and the statistic $\overline{X} - \overline{Y}$ can be used to test hypotheses about the values of μ_x and μ_y.

The central limit theorem tells you that, provided the sample sizes n_x and n_y are large, $\overline{X} - \overline{Y}$ will have a normal distribution whatever the distributions of X and Y. You can therefore use this to test whether there is a significant difference between the means of any two populations. The usual null hypothesis is that the values of μ_x and μ_y are equal, but other situations are possible provided that the null hypothesis gives you a value for $\mu_x - \mu_y$.

The **test statistic** you will need to use is based upon the distribution of $\overline{X} - \overline{Y}$ and is:

$$Z = \frac{\overline{X} - \overline{Y} - (\mu_x - \mu_y)}{\sqrt{\dfrac{\sigma_x^2}{n_x} + \dfrac{\sigma_y^2}{n_y}}}$$

Hint The formula for the test statistic is in the formula book.

- **Test for difference between two means:**
  - If $X \sim N(\mu_x, \sigma_x^2)$ and the independent random variable $Y \sim N(\mu_y, \sigma_y^2)$, then a test of the null hypothesis $H_0: \mu_x = \mu_y$ can be carried out using the test statistic:

    $$Z = \frac{\overline{X} - \overline{Y} - (\mu_x - \mu_y)}{\sqrt{\dfrac{\sigma_x^2}{n_x} + \dfrac{\sigma_y^2}{n_y}}}$$

  - If the sample sizes n_x and n_y are large, then the result can be extended, by the central limit theorem, to include cases where the distributions of X and Y are not normal.

Example **7** **SKILLS** REASONING/ARGUMENTATION

The weights of boys and girls in a certain school are known to be normally distributed with standard deviations of 5 kg and 8 kg respectively. A random sample of 25 boys had a mean weight of 48 kg and a random sample of 30 girls had a mean weight of 45 kg.

Stating your hypotheses clearly, test, at the 5% level of significance, whether there is evidence that the mean weight of the boys in the school is greater than the mean weight of the girls.

$H_0: \mu_{boy} = \mu_{girl} \qquad H_1: \mu_{boy} > \mu_{girl}$

$\sigma_1 = 5, n_1 = 25, \sigma_2 = 8$ and $n_2 = 30$

The value of the test statistic is:

$$z = \frac{\overline{x} - \overline{y} - (\mu_x - \mu_y)}{\sqrt{\dfrac{\sigma_x^2}{n_x} + \dfrac{\sigma_y^2}{n_y}}}$$

$$= \frac{48 - 45}{\sqrt{\dfrac{25}{25} + \dfrac{64}{30}}}$$

The alternative hypothesis is $\mu_{boy} > \mu_{girl}$, since this is what you are testing for. The null hypothesis is that the two population means are the same.

$\mu_x - \mu_y = 0$ from the null hypothesis

$$= \frac{3}{\sqrt{3.1333\ldots}}$$

$$= 1.6947\ldots$$

The 5% (one-tailed) critical value for Z is $z = 1.6449$ so this value is significant and you can reject H_0 and conclude that there is evidence that the mean weight of the boys is greater than the mean weight of the girls.

Watch out   Always write down (i.e. give a statement to support what you're saying) the **critical value** from the tables in full and give your conclusion in context.

Sometimes you may be asked to test, for example, whether the mean weight of the boys exceeds the mean weight of the girls by more than 2 kg. The test would be similar to the above but the hypotheses would be slightly different and this will affect the test statistic.

Example 8   **SKILLS**   ADAPTIVE LEARNING

The weights of boys and girls in a certain school are known to be normally distributed with standard deviations of 5 kg and 8 kg respectively. A random sample of 25 boys had a mean weight of 48 kg and a random sample of 30 girls had a mean weight of 45 kg.

Stating your hypotheses clearly, test, at the 5% level of significance, whether there is evidence that the mean weight of the boys in the school is more than 2 kg greater than the mean weight of the girls.

$H_0: \mu_{boy} - \mu_{girl} = 2$ $H_1: \mu_{boy} - \mu_{girl} > 2$

The null hypothesis is that the difference between the means is 2. The alternative hypothesis is that the difference is greater than 2.

$\sigma_1 = 5, n_1 = 25, s_2 = 8$ and $n_2 = 30$

The value of the test statistic is:

$$z = \frac{\bar{x} - \bar{y} - (\mu_x - \mu_y)}{\sqrt{\dfrac{\sigma_x^2}{n_x} + \dfrac{\sigma_y^2}{n_y}}}$$

$$= \frac{48 - 45 - 2}{\sqrt{\dfrac{25}{25} + \dfrac{64}{30}}}$$

Notice how the test statistic calculation has changed. This 2 comes from $\mu_x - \mu_y$.

$$= 0.565$$

The 5% (one-tailed) critical value for Z is $z = 1.6449$ so this value is not significant.

There is insufficient evidence that the mean weight of the boys is more than 2 kg greater than the mean weight of the girls.

Example 9

A manufacturer of drones can choose batteries made by two different companies. The standard deviation of lifetimes for *Never Die* batteries is 3.1 hours and for *Everlasting* batteries is 2.9 hours. A random sample of 80 *Never Die* batteries and a random sample of 90 *Everlasting* batteries were tested and their mean lifetimes were 7.9 hours and 8.2 hours respectively.

Stating your hypotheses clearly, test, at the 5% level of significance, whether there is evidence of a difference between the mean lifetimes of the two makes of batteries.

Let μ_x be the mean lifetime of *Never Die* batteries and let μ_y be the mean lifetime of *Everlasting* batteries.

H_0: $\mu_x = \mu_y$ H_1: $\mu_x \neq \mu_y$

$\sigma_x = 3.1$, $n_x = 80$, $\sigma_y = 2.9$ and $n_y = 90$

$\bar{x} - \bar{y} = 7.9 - 8.2 = -0.3$

So $z = \dfrac{\bar{x} - \bar{y} - (\mu_x - \mu_y)}{\sqrt{\dfrac{\sigma_x^2}{n_x} + \dfrac{\sigma_y^2}{n_y}}}$

$= \dfrac{-0.3}{\sqrt{\dfrac{(3.1)^2}{80} + \dfrac{(2.9)^2}{90}}}$

$= -0.649...$

The 5% (two-tailed) critical values for Z are $z = \pm 1.9600$.

So this value is not significant and you do not reject H_0. You can conclude that there is no significant evidence of a difference in the mean lifetimes of the two makes of batteries.

Watch out   You are testing for a **difference** (in either direction) between the means, so use a **two-tailed test**.

You are not told that the distributions of lifetimes of the batteries are normally distributed, but the sample sizes are both quite large, so by the central limit theorem you can proceed with $\bar{X} - \bar{Y}$ approximately normally distributed.

From the null hypothesis you know that $\mu_x - \mu_y = 0$.

Exercise 4E   **SKILLS**   REASONING/ARGUMENTATION

In Questions 1–3, carry out a test on the hypotheses at the given level of significance. The populations from which the random samples are drawn are normally distributed.

1 H_0: $\mu_1 = \mu_2$, H_1: $\mu_1 > \mu_2$, $n_1 = 15$, $\sigma_1 = 5.0$, $n_2 = 20$, $\sigma_2 = 4.8$, $\bar{x}_1 = 23.8$ and $\bar{x}_2 = 21.5$, using a 5% level.

2 H_0: $\mu_1 = \mu_2$, H_1: $\mu_1 \neq \mu_2$, $n_1 = 30$, $\sigma_1 = 4.2$, $n_2 = 25$, $\sigma_2 = 3.6$, $\bar{x}_1 = 49.6$ and $\bar{x}_2 = 51.7$, using a 5% level.

3 H_0: $\mu_1 = \mu_2$, H_1: $\mu_1 < \mu_2$, $n_1 = 25$, $\sigma_1 = 0.81$, $n_2 = 36$, $\sigma_2 = 0.75$, $\bar{x}_1 = 3.62$ and $\bar{x}_2 = 4.11$, using a 1% level.

In Questions 4–6, carry out a test on the hypotheses at the given level of significance. Given that the distributions of the populations are unknown, explain the significance of the central limit theorem in these tests.

4 $H_0: \mu_1 = \mu_2$, $H_1: \mu_1 \neq \mu_2$, $n_1 = 85$, $\sigma_1 = 8.2$, $n_2 = 100$, $\sigma_2 = 11.3$, $\bar{x}_1 = 112.0$ and $\bar{x}_2 = 108.1$, using a 1% level.

5 $H_0: \mu_1 = \mu_2$, $H_1: \mu_1 > \mu_2$, $n_1 = 100$, $\sigma_1 = 18.3$, $n_2 = 150$, $\sigma_2 = 15.4$, $\bar{x}_1 = 72.6$ and $\bar{x}_2 = 69.5$, using a 5% level.

6 $H_0: \mu_1 = \mu_2$, $H_1: \mu_1 < \mu_2$, $n_1 = 120$, $\sigma_1 = 0.013$, $n_2 = 90$, $\sigma_2 = 0.015$, $\bar{x}_1 = 0.863$ and $\bar{x}_2 = 0.868$, using a 1% level.

(E/P) **7** A factory has two machines designed to cut pipes. The first machine works to a standard deviation of 0.011 cm and the second machine has a standard deviation of 0.015 cm. A random sample of 10 pieces of pipe from the first machine has a mean length of 6.531 cm and a random sample of 15 pieces from the second machine has a mean length of 6.524 cm. Assuming that the lengths of pipe follow a normal distribution, test, at the 5% level, whether the machines are producing pipes of the same mean length. **(7 marks)**

(E/P) **8** A farmer grows wheat. He wants to improve his yield (the amount of something produced) per acre by at least 1 tonne, by buying a different variety of seed. The variance of the yield of the old seed is 0.6 tonnes² and the variance of the yield of the new seed is 0.8 tonnes². A random sample of 70 acres of wheat planted with the old seed has a mean yield of 5 tonnes and a random sample of 80 acres of wheat planted with the new seed has a mean yield of 6.5 tonnes.

   a Test, at the 5% level of significance, whether there is evidence that the mean yield of the new seed is more than 1 tonne greater than the mean yield of the old seed. State your hypotheses clearly. **(9 marks)**

SKILLS
   b Explain the relevance of the central limit theorem to the test in part **a**. **(2 marks)**

ANALYSIS

(E/P) **9** A farmer wanted to see if the diet of his cows influenced the amount of fat in their milk. The fat content of 60 litres of milk selected at random from cows fed entirely on grain had a mean value of 4.1 g per litre and a random sample of 50 litres of milk from cows fed on a combination of grain and grass had a mean value of 3.7 g per litre.

   It is known that the variance of fat content for a grain-only diet is 0.8 (g/l)² and that the variance of fat content for a grain and grass diet is 0.75 (g/l)².

   a Stating your hypotheses clearly and using a 5% level of significance, test whether there is a difference between the mean fat content of milk from cows fed on these two diets. **(7 marks)**

   b State, in the context of this question, an assumption you have made in carrying out the test in part **a**. **(1 mark)**

Challenge

SKILLS

ADAPTIVE
LEARNING;
CRITICAL
THINKING

Two independent random variables, X and Y, have unknown means μ_x and μ_y respectively. The variances σ_x^2 and σ_y^2 are both known. Random samples of n_x observations from the random variable X and n_y observations from the random variable Y are taken. The sample means are $\bar{x}$ and $\bar{y}$.

A hypothesis test is carried out to see if there is a difference in the means of the two samples and it is found that the null hypothesis is accepted.

A confidence interval is to be found for the common mean of the two samples, μ. $\hat{\mu}$ is used to denote the **pooled estimate of the population mean**, and is found by finding the mean of the combined samples.

a Show that $\hat{\mu} = \dfrac{n_x\bar{x} + n_y\bar{y}}{n_x + n_y}$

The distribution of the corresponding random variable is given as

$$N\left(\mu, \frac{n_x\,\sigma_x^2 + n_y\,\sigma_y^2}{(n_x + n_y)^2}\right)$$

Given that $n_x = 100$, $n_y = 120$, $\bar{x} = 46.0$, $\bar{y} = 47.0$, $\sigma_x^2 = 16.0$ and $\sigma_y^2 = 24.0$,

b find the 99% confidence interval for μ.

4.6 Use of large sample results for an unknown population

One of the practical difficulties that you will encounter when carrying out hypothesis tests based on samples (and also in finding confidence intervals) is the need to know the value of the population standard deviation. In practice, if you do not know μ, it is unlikely that you will know σ. Sometimes it is reasonable to assume that similar processes or populations will have the same standard deviation but perhaps just have an altered mean. Occasionally, you can look at historical data and see that over a period of time, the standard deviation has been constant. It may also be reasonable to assume that it remains constant but often it may be impossible to choose a reliable value of σ.

In situations such as this, you can use the central limit theorem and the sample variance s^2, which is an unbiased estimator of the population variance.

- If the population is normal, or can be assumed to be so, then, for large samples, $\dfrac{\bar{X} - \mu}{\frac{s}{\sqrt{n}}}$ has an approximate $N(0, 1^2)$ distribution.

Watch out Both of these tests rely on large sample sizes, and the second test also relies on the central limit theorem.

- If the population is not normal, by assuming that s is a close approximation to σ, then for large samples, $\dfrac{\bar{X} - \mu}{\frac{s}{\sqrt{n}}}$ can be treated as having an approximate $N(0, 1^2)$ distribution.

Example (10)   **SKILLS**   REASONING/ARGUMENTATION

As part of a study of the health of young children, a random sample of 220 children from area A and a second, independent random sample of 180 children from area B were weighed.
The results are given in the table below.

	n	$\bar{x}$	s
Area A	220	37.8	3.6
Area B	180	38.6	4.1

a Test, at the 5% level of significance, whether there is evidence of a difference in the mean weight of children in the two areas. State your hypotheses clearly.

b State an assumption you have made in carrying out this test.

c Explain the significance of the central limit theorem to this test.

---

a $H_0 : \mu_A = \mu_B$ $H_1 : \mu_A \neq \mu_B$

State the hypotheses in terms of μ. The word 'difference' suggests a two-tailed test.

Test statistic $z = \dfrac{\bar{x}_A - \bar{x}_B - (\mu_A - \mu_B)}{\sqrt{\dfrac{\sigma_A^2}{n_A} + \dfrac{\sigma_B^2}{n_B}}}$

$z = \dfrac{38.6 - 37.8}{\sqrt{\dfrac{3.6^2}{220} + \dfrac{4.1^2}{180}}}$

For a two-tailed test you can choose whether to use $\bar{x}_A - \bar{x}_B$ or $\bar{x}_B - \bar{x}_A$. It is usually easier to choose the case which gives a positive value to the test statistic, which is $\bar{x}_B - \bar{x}_A$ in this case.

$z = 2.0499...$
$\quad = 2.05$ (3 s.f.)

Give the value to at least 3 s.f.

Two-tail 5% critical values are $z = \pm 1.96$

Since $2.05 > 1.96$, the result is significant so reject H_0.

Always state the critical value(s).

There is evidence that the mean weight of children in the two areas is different.

Always give your conclusion in context.

b The test statistic requires σ so you have to assume that $s^2 = \sigma^2$ for both samples.

c You are not told that the populations are normally distributed but the samples are both large and so the central limit theorem enables us to assume that $\overline{X}_A$ and $\overline{X}_B$ are both normal.

Watch out Note that the central limit theorem is not an assumption – it is a theorem that can be invoked to enable you to use the normal distribution.

The assumption that $s^2 = \sigma^2$ is reasonable since both samples are large.

Exercise **4F** **SKILLS** REASONING/ARGUMENTATION

(E/P) **1** An experiment was carried out to compare the drying properties of two paints, *Quickdry* and *Speedicover*. In the experiment, 200 similar pieces of metal were painted, 100 randomly allocated to *Quickdry* and the rest to *Speedicover*. The table below summarises the times, in minutes, taken for these pieces of metal to become touch-dry.

	Quickdry	*Speedicover*
Mean	28.7	30.6
Standard deviation	7.32	3.51

Using a 5% significance level, test whether the mean time for *Quickdry* to become touch-dry is less than that for *Speedicover*. State your hypotheses clearly. **(6 marks)**

(E/P) **2** A supermarket examined a random sample of 80 weekend shoppers' purchases and an independent random sample of 120 weekday shoppers' purchases. The results are summarised in the table below.

	n	$\bar{x}$	s
Weekend	80	38.64	6.59
Weekday	120	40.13	8.23

a Stating your hypotheses clearly, test, at the 5% level of significance, whether there is evidence that the mean expenditure during the week is more than at weekends. **(6 marks)**

b State an assumption you have made in carrying out this test. **(1 mark)**

(E/P) **3** It is claimed that the **components** produced in a small factory have a mean mass of 10 g.

A random sample of 250 of these components is tested and the sample mean $\bar{x}$ is 9.88 g and the standard deviation s is 1.12 g.

a Test, at the 5% level, whether there has been a change in the mean mass of a component. **(6 marks)**

b State any assumptions you would make to carry out this test. **(1 mark)**

Chapter review **4**

(E) **1** A random sample of 100 observations is taken from a probability distribution with mean 5 and variance 1. Estimate the probability that the mean of the sample is greater than 5.2 **(3 marks)**

(E/P) **2** A fair six-sided dice numbered 1, 2, 4, 5, 7, 8 is rolled 20 times. Estimate the probability that the average score is less than 4. **(4 marks)**

(E/P) **3** A sample of size n is taken from a normal distribution with $\mu = 1$ and $\sigma = 1$. Find the minimum sample size such that the probability of the sample mean being negative is less than 5%. **(3 marks)**

E/P 4 In a group of 20 students, each rolls a fair six-sided dice 10 times and records the number of sixes. Estimate the probability that the average number of sixes rolled by each student is greater than 2. **(4 marks)**

E 5 Buses arrive at a bus stop on average once every 5 minutes.

   a Find the probability that exactly 3 buses arrive in the next 10 minutes. **(2 marks)**

   b Use the central limit theorem to estimate the probability that at least 25 buses arrive in the next 2 hours. **(3 marks)**

E/P 6 The masses of eggs are normally distributed with mean 60 g and standard deviation 5 g. A box contains 48 randomly chosen eggs.

   a Calculate the probability that the mean mass of an egg in a randomly chosen box is greater than 59 g. **(3 marks)**

   b State, with a reason, whether your answer to part **a** is an estimate. **(1 mark)**

   The probability that an egg has a double yolk is 0.1. A sample of 30 boxes is taken.

   c Estimate the probability that the sample will contain fewer than 150 double-yolk eggs in total. **(5 marks)**

E/P 7 An automatic coffee machine uses milk powder. The mass, S grams, of milk powder used in one cup of coffee is modelled by $S \sim N(4.9, 0.8^2)$.

   Milk powder is sold in 500 g packs. Find the probability that one pack will be sufficient for 100 cups of coffee. **(4 marks)**

E/P 8 A random sample of size n is to be taken from a population with mean 40 and variance 9. Find the minimum sample size such that the probability of the sample mean being greater than 42 is less than 5%. **(5 marks)**

E 9 A sample of size 20 is taken from a population with an unknown distribution, with mean 35 and variance 9. Find the probability that the sample mean will be greater than 37. **(3 marks)**

E/P 10 A nationwide survey asked 500 people whether they prefer white chocolate or milk chocolate. The survey company wants to determine whether the proportion of people who prefer milk chocolate differs significantly from 60%.

   The survey company assumes that in the population, 60% of people prefer milk chocolate, and defines the random variable X to take the value 1 if a randomly selected member of the population prefers milk chocolate, and 0 otherwise.

   a Describe the distribution of X and state its mean and variance. **(3 marks)**

   Modelling the survey as a random sample of size 500 from the distribution in part **a**,

   b estimate the probability that the sample mean differs from 0.6 by 0.03 or more. **(3 marks)**

   c How many people should be surveyed in order for there to be a greater than 95% chance that the sample mean differs from 0.6 by at most 0.03? **(5 marks)**

(E) **11** The breaking stresses of rubber bands are normally distributed.

A company uses bands with a mean breaking stress of 46.50 N.

A new supplier claims that they can supply bands that are stronger and provides a sample of 100 bands for the company to test. The company checked the breaking stress X for each of these 100 bands and the results are summarised as follows:

$$n = 100 \quad \Sigma X = 4715 \quad \Sigma X^2 = 222\,910$$

Test, at the 5% level, whether there is evidence that the new bands are stronger.   **(6 marks)**

(E) **12** The amount, to the nearest mg, of a certain chemical in particles in the atmosphere at a meteorological station was measured each day for 300 days. The results are shown in the table.

Amount of chemical (mg)	12	13	14	15	16
Number of days	5	42	210	31	12

Estimate the mean amount of this chemical in the atmosphere, and find, to 2 decimal places, the standard error of this estimate.   **(3 marks)**

(E) **13** The times taken by five-year-old children to complete a certain task are normally distributed with a standard deviation of 8.0 s. A random sample of 25 five-year-old children from school A were given this task and their mean time was 44.2 s.

The mean time for a random sample of 20 five-year-old children from school B was 40.9 s.

The headteacher of school B concluded that the overall mean for school B must be less than that of school A.

Given that the two samples were independent, test the headteacher's conclusion using a 5% significance level. State your hypotheses clearly.   **(6 marks)**

(E/P) **14** A garage sells both leaded and unleaded fuel. The distribution of the values of sales for each fuel type is normal. During 2010, the standard deviation of individual sales of each type of fuel was £3.25. The mean of the individual sales of leaded fuel during this time was £8.72.

A random sample of 100 individual sales of unleaded fuel gave a mean of £9.71.

The mean of the sales of unleaded fuel for 2009 was £9.10.

Using a 5% significance level, investigate whether there is sufficient evidence to conclude that the mean of all the 2010 unleaded fuel sales was greater than the mean of the 2009 sales.   **(6 marks)**

(E/P) **15** A cardiologist claims that there is a higher mean heart rate in people who always drive to work compared to people who regularly walk to work. She measures the heart rates X of 30 people who always drive to work and 36 people who regularly walk to work. Her results are summarised in the table below.

	n	$\overline{X}$	s^2
Drive to work	30	52	60.2
Walk to work	36	47	55.8

a Test, at the 5% level of significance, the cardiologist's claim.

State your hypotheses clearly.   **(6 marks)**

b State any assumptions you have made in testing the cardiologist's claim.   **(2 marks)**

The cardiologist decides to add another person who drives to work to her data. She measures the person's heart rate and finds $X = 55$.

c Find an unbiased estimate of the variance for the sample of 31 people who drive to work.

Give your answer to 3 significant figures.   **(4 marks)**

Challenge

SKILLS

PROBLEM-SOLVING; ANALYSIS

Let $X_1, ..., X_n$ be a random sample from a population with distribution N(μ, σ^2). Show that $\overline{X} \sim N\left(\mu, \dfrac{\sigma^2}{n}\right)$.

Hint You can use the fact that if $X_1 \sim N(\mu_1, \sigma_1^2)$ and $X_2 \sim N(\mu_2, \sigma_2^2)$ are independent, then $X_1 + X_2 \sim N(\mu_1 + \mu_2, \sigma_1^2 + \sigma_2^2)$.

Summary of key points

1 The **central limit theorem** states that, given a random sample of size n from any distribution with mean μ and variance σ^2, the sample mean $\overline{X}$ is approximately distributed as $N\left(\mu, \dfrac{\sigma^2}{n}\right)$.

2 Test for difference between two means:

- If $X \sim N(\mu_x, \sigma_x^2)$ and the independent random variable $Y \sim N(\mu_y, \sigma_y^2)$, then a test of the null hypothesis H$_0$: $\mu_x = \mu_y$ can be carried out using the test statistic:

$$Z = \frac{\overline{X} - \overline{Y} - (\mu_x - \mu_y)}{\sqrt{\dfrac{\sigma_x^2}{n_x} + \dfrac{\sigma_y^2}{n_y}}}$$

- If the sample sizes n_x and n_y are large then the result can be extended, by the central limit theorem, to include cases where the distributions of X and Y are not normal.

- If the population is normal, or can be assumed to be so, then, for large samples, $\dfrac{\overline{X} - \mu}{\dfrac{s}{\sqrt{n}}}$ has an approximate $N(0, 1^2)$ distribution.

- If the population is not normal, by assuming that s is a close approximation to σ, then $\dfrac{\overline{X} - \mu}{\dfrac{s}{\sqrt{n}}}$ can be treated as having an approximate $N(0, 1^2)$ distribution.

5 CORRELATION

Learning objectives

After completing this chapter you should be able to:

● Calculate and interpret Spearman's rank correlation coefficient → pages 71–76

● Carry out hypothesis tests for zero correlation using either Spearman's rank correlation coefficient or the product moment correlation coefficient → pages 77–82

Prior knowledge check

1 The scatter diagram shows data on the age and value of a particular model of car.

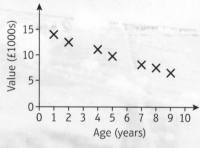

a Describe the type of correlation shown.

b Interpret the correlation in context. ← Statistics 1 Section 5.1

2 A set of 8 bivariate data points (x, y) is summarised using $\sum x = 48$, $\sum y = 92$, $\sum x^2 = 340$, $\sum y^2 = 1142$ and $\sum xy = 616$.

Calculate:

a S_{xx} b S_{yy} c S_{xy} ← Statistics 1 Section 5.3

Spearman's rank correlation coefficient can be used to determine the degree to which two ice skating judges agree or disagree about the relative performance of the skaters. It considers rankings rather than specific values. → Exercise 5A Q8

5.1 Spearman's rank correlation coefficient

In the Statistics 1 book, you used the product moment correlation coefficient r as a measure of the strength of **linear correlation** between paired observations (x_i, y_i). In cases where the correlation is not linear, or where the data are not measurable on a **continuous** scale, the PMCC may not be a good measure of the correlation between two variables.

For example, suppose a manufacturer of tea produced a number of different blends; you could taste each blend and place the blends in **rank** order, most liked to least liked. However, you do not have a continuous numerical scale for measuring your ranking. In a different example, it may be quicker to arrange a group of individuals in order of height than to measure each one. Under these circumstances, Spearman's rank correlation coefficient is used.

Spearman's rank correlation coefficient is denoted by r_s. It is a special case of the product moment correlation coefficient in which the data are converted to **rankings** before calculating the coefficient.

- To **rank** two sets of data, X and Y, you give the rank 1 to the highest of the x_i values, 2 to the next highest, 3 to the next highest, and so on. You do the same for the y_i values.

> **Notation**   It makes no difference if you rank the smallest as 1, the next smallest as 2, etc., provided you do the same to both X and Y.

Spearman's rank correlation coefficient can be used instead of the product moment correlation coefficient if one of the following conditions is true:

   one or both data sets are not from a normally distributed population

   there is a non-linear relationship between the two data sets

   one or both data sets already represent a ranking (as in Example 1).

Spearman's rank correlation coefficient is calculated using the PMCC formula, except that the ranks of the data are used. As such:

- A Spearman's rank correlation coefficient of:
  - +1 means that rankings are in perfect agreement
  - −1 means that the rankings are in exact reverse order
  - 0 means that there is no correlation between the rankings.

You can calculate Spearman's rank correlation coefficient more quickly by looking at the **differences** between the ranks of each observation.

- If there are no tied ranks, Spearman's rank correlation coefficient r_s is calculated using

$$r_s = 1 - \frac{6\sum d^2}{n(n^2 - 1)}$$

where d is the difference between the ranks of each observation, and n is the number of pairs of observations.

> **Notation**   **Tied ranks** occur when two or more data values in one of the data sets are the same.

Example 1

Two tea tasters were asked to rank nine blends of tea in order of preference.
The tea they liked best was ranked 1. The table shows their orders of preference:

Blend	A	B	C	D	E	F	G	H	I
Taster 1 (x)	3	6	2	8	5	9	7	1	4
Taster 2 (y)	5	6	4	2	7	8	9	1	3

Calculate Spearman's rank correlation coefficient for these data.

Blend	A	B	C	D	E	F	G	H	I
Taster 1	3	6	2	8	5	9	7	1	4
Taster 2	5	6	4	2	7	8	9	1	3
d	−2	0	−2	6	−2	1	−2	0	1
d^2	4	0	4	36	4	1	4	0	1

Find the difference between each pair. It is useful to keep the negative signs to check, since they must all add to 0.

$\sum d^2 = 54$

$$r_s = 1 - \frac{6\sum d^2}{n(n^2 - 1)}$$

$$r_s = 1 - \frac{6 \times 54}{9(9^2 - 1)}$$

$$r_s = 0.55$$

Find the sum of d^2

Use the standard formula to find r_s

Example 2 **SKILLS** **INTERPRETATION**

During a country farm show, two judges ranked ten horses on their overall performances.
The table here shows the judges' rankings:

Cattle	A	B	C	D	E	F	G	H	I	J
Judge A	1	5	2	6	4	8	3	7	10	9
Judge B	3	6	2	7	5	8	1	4	9	10

Find Spearman's rank correlation coefficient between the two judges and comment on the result.

A	B	d	d^2
1	3	−2	4
5	6	−1	1
2	2	0	0
6	7	−1	1
4	5	−1	1
8	8	0	0
3	1	2	4
7	4	3	9
10	9	1	1
9	10	−1	1
	Total		22

These data are already ranked and there are no tied ranks.

Find d and d^2 for each pair of ranks.

Find $\sum d^2$

$$r_s = 1 - \frac{6 \times 22}{10(100 - 1)} = 0.867 \longleftarrow$$

Calculate r_s

There is a reasonable degree of agreement between the two judges.

Draw a conclusion.

If you are ranking data, and two or more data values are equal, then these data values will have a **tied rank**.

- **Equal data values should be assigned a rank equal to the mean of the tied ranks.**

For example:

Data value	200	350	350	400	700	800	800	800	1200
Rank	1	2.5	2.5	4	5	7	7	7	9

The 2nd and 3rd rank are tied, so assign a rank of 2.5 to each of these data values.

The 6th, 7th and 8th ranks are tied, so assign a rank of $\frac{6 + 7 + 8}{3} = 7$ to each of these data values.

When ranks are tied, the formula for the Spearman's rank correlation coefficient will not be correct and you will be required to use the PMCC formula instead.

You will not be expected to calculate a measure of correlation with tied ranks, but you are expected to know how to deal with tied ranks.

The example is valid to see what happens, but a typical exam question will not require the calculation.

Example ③ **SKILLS** PROBLEM-SOLVING

The marks of eight students in French and German tests were as follows:

	A	B	C	D	E	F	G	H
French, $f\%$	52	25	86	33	55	55	54	46
German, $g\%$	40	48	65	57	40	39	63	34

Find a measure of correlation, showing clearly how you deal with tied ranks.
Give your answer to 3 decimal places.

	A	B	C	D	E	F	G	H
French (f)	4	1	8	2	⑥	⑥	5	3
German (g)	③	6	5	8	③	2	7	1

Rank the data.

	A	B	C	D	E	F	G	H
French (f)	4	1	8	2	6.5	6.5	5	3
German (g)	3.5	6	5	8	3.5	2	7	1

There are tied ranks in both rows.

E and F for French will both be given a rank of 6.5

A and E for German will both be given a rank of 3.5

$$\sum f = 36$$
$$\sum g = 36$$
$$\sum f^2 = 203.5$$
$$\sum g^2 = 203.5$$
$$\sum fg = 149.75$$

Since we have tied ranks, we must use the PMCC formula on the ranks. The calculation of the PMCC is not required.

$$S_{ff} = \sum f^2 - \frac{(\sum f)^2}{n} = 203.5 - \frac{36^2}{8} = 41.5$$

$$S_{gg} = \sum g^2 - \frac{(\sum g)^2}{n} = 203.5 - \frac{36^2}{8} = 41.5$$

$$S_{fg} = \sum fg - \frac{(\sum f)(\sum g)}{n} = 149.75 - \frac{36 \times 36}{8} = -12.25$$

$$r_s = \frac{S_{fg}}{\sqrt{S_{ff} S_{gg}}} = \frac{-12.25}{\sqrt{41.5} \times 41.5} = -0.295 \ (3 \ d.p.)$$

Exercise 5A **SKILLS** REASONING/ARGUMENTATION

(P) **1** The scatter graph shows the length, l m, and mass, m kg, of 10 randomly selected male Siberian tigers.

Agnese wants to analyse the correlation between l and m. Give one reason why she might choose to use:

a the product moment correlation coefficient

b Spearman's rank correlation coefficient.

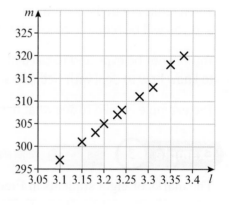

(P) **2** A college dean is trying to determine if a published placement test (PPT) gives a good indicator of the likely student performance in a final exam. Data on past performances are shown in the scatter graph:

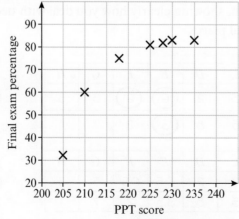

Give a reason why the dean should not use the product moment correlation coefficient to measure the strength of the correlation of the two variables.

(P)   **3** A sports science researcher is investigating whether there is a correlation between the height of a basketball player and the number of attempts it takes the player to score a free throw. The researcher proposes to collect a random sample of data and then calculate the product moment correlation coefficient between the two variables.

Give a reason why the PMCC would not be appropriate in this situation and state an alternative method that the researcher can use.

4 For each of the data sets of ranks below, calculate Spearman's rank correlation coefficient and interpret the result.

a

r_x	1	2	3	4	5	6
r_y	3	2	1	5	4	6

b

r_x	1	2	3	4	5	6	7	8	9	10
r_y	2	1	4	3	5	8	7	9	6	10

c

r_x	5	2	6	1	4	3	7	8
r_y	5	6	3	8	7	4	2	1

5 Match the scatter graphs with the given values of Spearman's rank correlation coefficient.

a

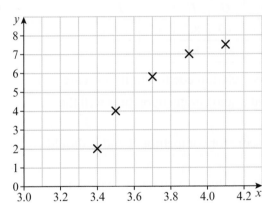

b

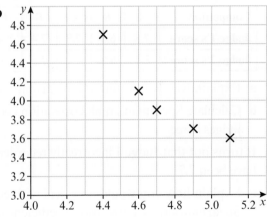

c

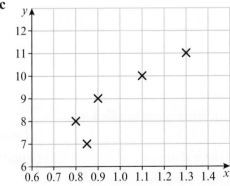

d

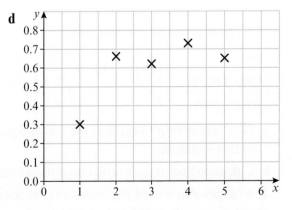

$$r_s = -1 \qquad r_s = 0.9 \qquad r_s = 1 \qquad r_s = 0.5$$

(E) **6** The number of goals scored by football teams and their positions in the league were recorded as follows for the top 12 teams.

Team	A	B	C	D	E	F	G	H	I	J	K	L
Goals	49	44	43	36	40	39	29	21	28	30	33	26
League position	1	2	3	4	5	6	7	8	9	10	11	12

     a Find $\sum d^2$, where d is the difference between the ranks of each observation. **(3 marks)**

     b Calculate Spearman's rank correlation coefficient for these data.
What conclusions can be drawn from this result? **(3 marks)**

7 An experienced veterinary surgeon and a trainee veterinary surgeon each rank eight rabbits on their overall health. Their rankings are shown below.

Rabbit	A	D	F	E	B	C	H	G
Qualified vet	1	2	3	4	5	6	7	8
Trainee vet	1	2	5	6	4	3	8	7

Find Spearman's rank correlation coefficient for these data, and comment on the experience of the trainee vet.

(P) **8** Two judges at an ice dancing competition awarded marks as follows.

Competitor	A	B	C	D	E	F	G	H	I	J
Judge 1's score	7.8	6.6	7.3	7.4	8.4	6.5	8.9	8.5	6.7	7.7
Judge 2's score	8.1	6.8	8.2	7.5	8.0	6.7	8.5	8.3	6.6	7.8

     a Explain why you would use Spearman's rank correlation coefficient in this case.

     b Calculate Spearman's rank correlation coefficient r_s and comment on how well the judges agree.

It turns out that Judge 1 incorrectly recorded her score for competitor A and it should have been 7.7.

     c Explain how you would now deal with equal data values if you had to calculate Spearman's rank correlation coefficient again.

(E) **9** In a diving competition, two judges scored each of 7 divers on a forward somersault.

Diver	A	B	C	D	E	F	G
Judge 1 score	4.5	5.1	5.2	5.2	5.4	5.7	5.8
Judge 2 score	5.2	4.8	4.9	5.1	5.0	5.3	5.4

     a Give one reason to support the use of Spearman's rank correlation coefficient in this scenario. **(1 mark)**

     b Calculate Spearman's rank correlation coefficient for these data. **(4 marks)**

The judges also scored the divers on a backward somersault. Spearman's rank correlation coefficient for their ranks in this case was 0.676

     c Compare the judges' ranks for the two dives. **(1 mark)**

5.2 Hypothesis testing for zero correlation

You might need to carry out a **hypothesis test** to find whether the correlation for a particular sample indicates that there is a non-zero correlation for the whole population. Hypothesis tests for zero correlation can use either the product moment correlation coefficient or Spearman's rank correlation coefficient.

To test whether the population correlation ρ is greater than zero, or to test whether the population correlation ρ is less than zero, use a **one-tailed test:**

Notation r is usually used to denote the correlation for a **sample**. The Greek letter rho (ρ) is used to denote the correlation for the **whole population**. If you need to distinguish between the PMCC and Spearman's rank correlation coefficient, use r and ρ for the PMCC and use r_s and ρ_s for Spearman's.

- For a one-tailed test, use either:
  - $H_0 : \rho = 0$, $H_1 : \rho > 0$ or
  - $H_0 : \rho = 0$, $H_1 : \rho < 0$

To test whether the population correlation is not equal to zero, use a **two-tailed test:**

- For a two-tailed test, use:
  - $H_0 : \rho = 0$, $H_1 : \rho \neq 0$

Determine the **critical region** for r or r_s using the tables of critical values given in the formulae booklet and on page 143, or using your calculator. This is the table of critical values for the product moment correlation coefficient.

Watch out The table for Spearman's rank correlation coefficient is different. Read the question carefully and choose the correct table.

Product moment coefficient					
Level					**Sample size**
0.10	**0.05**	**0.025**	**0.01**	**0.005**	
0.8000	0.9000	0.9500	0.9800	0.9900	4
0.6870	0.8054	0.8783	0.9343	0.9587	5
0.6084	0.7293	0.8114	0.8822	0.9172	6
0.5509	0.6694	0.7545	0.8329	0.8745	7
0.5067	0.6215	0.7067	0.7887	0.8343	8
0.4716	0.5822	0.6664	0.7498	0.7977	9

For a sample size of 8, the critical value of r to be significant at the 5% level on a one-tailed test is 0.6215. A value of r greater than 0.6215 from a sample of size 8 would provide sufficient evidence to reject the null hypothesis and conclude that $\rho > 0$. An observed value of r less than -0.6215 would provide sufficient evidence to conclude that $\rho < 0$.

Example **4** **SKILLS** REASONING/ARGUMENTATION

A chemist observed 20 reactions, and recorded the mass of the reactant, x grams, and the duration of a reaction, y minutes.

She summarised her findings as follows:

$$\sum x = 20 \quad \sum y = 35 \quad \sum xy = 65 \quad \sum x^2 = 35 \quad \sum y^2 = 130$$

Test, at the 5% significance level, whether these results show evidence of any correlation between the mass of the reactant and the duration of the reaction.

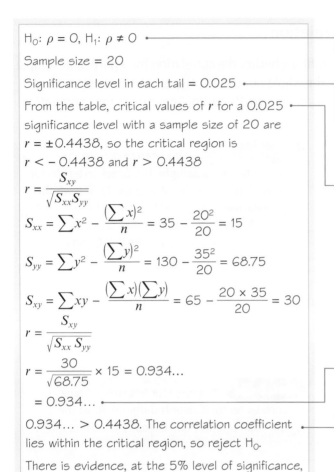

$H_0: \rho = 0, H_1: \rho \neq 0$

Sample size = 20

Significance level in each tail = 0.025

From the table, critical values of r for a 0.025 significance level with a sample size of 20 are $r = \pm 0.4438$, so the critical region is $r < -0.4438$ and $r > 0.4438$

$r = \dfrac{S_{xy}}{\sqrt{S_{xx}S_{yy}}}$

$S_{xx} = \sum x^2 - \dfrac{(\sum x)^2}{n} = 35 - \dfrac{20^2}{20} = 15$

$S_{yy} = \sum y^2 - \dfrac{(\sum y)^2}{n} = 130 - \dfrac{35^2}{20} = 68.75$

$S_{xy} = \sum xy - \dfrac{(\sum x)(\sum y)}{n} = 65 - \dfrac{20 \times 35}{20} = 30$

$r = \dfrac{S_{xy}}{\sqrt{S_{xx}\, S_{yy}}}$

$r = \dfrac{30}{\sqrt{68.75}} \times 15 = 0.934\ldots$

$\quad = 0.934\ldots$

0.934... > 0.4438. The correlation coefficient lies within the critical region, so reject H_0.

There is evidence, at the 5% level of significance, that there is a correlation between the mass of the reactant and the duration of the reaction.

You are testing for **any** correlation, not for positive or negative correlation, so use a **two-tailed** test.

This is a two-tailed test so halve the significance level to find the probability in each tail.

Use the table of critical values on page 143 to find the critical region.

Use the given summary statistics to calculate r.

You reject H_0 if the observed value lies inside the critical region.

Write a conclusion in the context of the original question.

You can carry out a hypothesis test for zero correlation using Spearman's rank correlation coefficient in the same way. The table of critical values for Spearman's coefficient is also given in the formulae booklet and on page 143.

Sample size	Spearman's coefficient		
	Level		
	0.05	0.025	0.01
4	1.0000	–	–
5	0.9000	1.0000	1.0000
6	0.8286	0.8857	0.9429
7	0.7143	0.7857	0.8929
8	0.6429	0.7381	0.8333
9	0.6000	0.7000	0.7833

For a sample size of 8, you see from the table that the critical value of r_s to be significant at the 0.025 level on a one-tailed test is ± 0.7381

Example (5)   **SKILLS**   REASONING/ARGUMENTATION

The popularity of 16 subjects at a school was found by counting the number of boys and the number of girls who chose each subject and then ranking the subjects. The results are shown in the table below.

Subject	A	B	C	D	E	F	G	H	I	J	K	L	M	N	O	P
Boys' ranks, b	2	5	9	8	1	3	15	16	6	10	12	14	4	7	11	13
Girls' ranks, g	4	7	11	3	6	9	12	16	5	13	10	8	2	1	15	14

a Calculate Spearman's rank correlation coefficient.

b Using a suitable test at the 1% level of significance, test the claim that boys' and girls' choices are positively correlated.

a

Subject	A	B	C	D	E	F	G	H	I	J	K	L	M	N	O	P
Boys' ranks, b	2	5	9	8	1	3	15	16	6	10	12	14	4	7	11	13
Girls' ranks, g	4	7	11	3	6	9	12	16	5	13	10	8	2	1	15	14
d	−2	−2	−2	5	−5	−6	3	0	1	−3	2	6	2	6	−4	−1
d^2	4	4	4	25	25	36	9	0	1	9	4	36	4	36	16	1

> Extend the table to include rows for d and d^2.

$\sum d^2 = 214$

$r_s = 1 - \dfrac{6\sum d^2}{n(n^2 - 1)}$

$\quad = 1 - \dfrac{6 \times 214}{16(16^2 - 1)}$

$\quad = 0.685\ldots$

b $H_0: \rho = 0$

$\quad H_1: \rho > 0$

> State your hypotheses. You are testing for positive correlation so this is a one-tailed test.

From the tables for a sample size of 16 the critical value is 0.5824.

Since 0.685... > 0.5824, the result is significant at the 1% level.

> Find the critical value.

> See if your value of r_s is significant.

Reject H_0

There is evidence that boys' and girls' choices are positively correlated.

> Draw a conclusion.

Exercise **5B** **SKILLS** REASONING/ARGUMENTATION

1 A sample of 7 observations (x, y) was taken, and the following values were calculated:

$$\sum x = 29 \quad \sum x^2 = 131 \quad \sum y = 28 \quad \sum y^2 = 140 \quad \sum xy = 99$$

a Calculate the product moment correlation coefficient for this sample.

b Test H_0: $\rho = 0$ against H_1: $\rho \neq 0$. Use a 1% significance level and state any assumptions that you have made.

(E) **2** The ages, X years, and heights, Y cm, of 11 members of an athletics club were recorded and the following statistics were used to summarise the results.

$$\sum X = 168 \quad \sum Y = 1275 \quad \sum XY = 20\,704 \quad \sum X^2 = 2585 \quad \sum Y^2 = 320\,019$$

a Calculate the product moment correlation coefficient for these data. **(3 marks)**

b Test the assertion that the ages and heights of the club members are positively correlated. State your conclusion in words and any assumptions you have made. Use a 5% level of significance. **(5 marks)**

3 A sample of 30 cars were ranked by engine size and by fuel economy (distance travelled per unit volume of fuel used).

A consumer group wants to test whether fuel economy and engine size are related.

a Find the critical region for a hypothesis test based on Spearman's rank correlation coefficient. Use a 5% level of significance.

A Spearman's rank correlation coefficient of $r_s = 0.5321$ was calculated for the sample.

b Comment on this value in light of your answer to part **a**.

(E/P) **4** For one of the activities at a gymnastics competition, 8 gymnasts were awarded marks out of 10 for technical ability and artistic performance. The results were as follows.

SKILLS
CRITICAL
THINKING

Gymnast	A	B	C	D	E	F	G	H
Technical ability	8.5	8.6	9.5	7.5	6.8	9.1	9.4	9.2
Artistic performance	6.2	7.5	8.2	6.7	6.0	7.2	8.0	9.1

The value of the product moment correlation coefficient for these data is 0.774

a Stating your hypotheses clearly, and using a 1% level of significance, test for evidence of a positive association between technical ability and artistic performance. Interpret this value. **(4 marks)**

b Calculate the value of Spearman's rank correlation coefficient for these data. **(3 marks)**

c Give one reason why a hypothesis test based on Spearman's rank correlation coefficient might be more suitable for this data set. **(1 mark)**

d Use your answer to part **b** to carry out a second hypothesis test for evidence of a positive correlation between technical ability and artistic performance. Use a 1% significance level. **(4 marks)**

(E/P) 5 Two judges ranked 8 ice skaters in a competition according to the table below.

Skater / Judge	i	ii	iii	iv	v	vi	vii	viii
A	2	5	3	7	8	1	4	6
B	3	2	6	5	7	4	1	8

A test is to be carried out to see if there is a positive association between the rankings of the judges.

a Give a reason to support the use of Spearman's rank correlation coefficient in this case. **(1 mark)**

b Calculate Spearman's rank correlation coefficient. **(3 marks)**

c Carry out the test at the 5% level of significance, stating your hypotheses clearly. **(4 marks)**

(P) 6 Each of the teams in a school hockey league had the total number of goals scored by them and against them recorded, with the following results.

Team	A	B	C	D	E	F	G
Goals for	39	40	28	27	26	30	42
Goals against	22	28	27	42	24	38	23

By using Spearman's rank correlation coefficient, investigate whether there is any association between goals for and goals against. Use a suitable test at the 1% level to investigate the statement, '*A team that scores a lot of goals concedes very few goals*'.

(E) 7 The weekly takings (the amount of money received) and weekly profits for six different branches of a kebab restaurant are shown in the table below.

Shop	1	2	3	4	5	6
Takings (£)	400	6200	3600	5100	5000	3800
Profits (£)	400	1100	450	750	800	500

a Calculate Spearman's rank correlation coefficient r_s between the takings and the profit. **(3 marks)**

b Test, at the 5% significance level, the assertion that profits and takings are positively correlated. **(4 marks)**

(E) 8 The rankings of 12 students in Mathematics and Music were as follows.

Mathematics	1	2	3	4	5	6	7	8	9	10	11	12
Music	6	4	2	3	1	7	5	9	10	8	11	12

a Calculate Spearman's rank correlation coefficient r_s, showing your value of $\sum d^2$. **(3 marks)**

b Test whether there is a correlation between these subjects. State the null and alternative hypotheses used. Use a 5% significance level. **(4 marks)**

9 A child is asked to place 10 objects in order and gives the ordering:

$$A \quad C \quad H \quad F \quad B \quad D \quad G \quad E \quad J \quad I$$

The correct ordering is:

$$A \quad B \quad C \quad D \quad E \quad F \quad G \quad H \quad I \quad J$$

Carry out a suitable hypothesis test at the 5% level of significance to determine whether there is a positive association between the child's order and the correct ordering. You must state clearly which correlation coefficient you are using and justify your selection. **(8 marks)**

10 The crop of a root vegetable was measured over six **consecutive** years, the years being ranked for wetness. The results are given in the table below.

Year	1	2	3	4	5	6
Crop (10 000 tons)	62	73	52	77	63	61
Rank of wetness	5	4	1	6	3	2

A farmer claims that crop yield and wetness are not correlated. Test this assertion using a 5% significance level. You must state which correlation coefficient you are using and justify your selection. **(8 marks)**

11 A researcher collects data on the heights and masses of a random sample of gorillas. She finds that the correlation coefficient between the data is 0.546

a Explain which measure of correlation the researcher is likely to have used.

Given that the value of the correlation coefficient provided sufficient evidence to accept the alternative hypothesis that there is positive correlation between the variables,

b find the smallest possible significance level, given that she collected data from 14 gorillas

c find the smallest possible sample size, given that she carried out the test at the 5% level of significance.

Chapter review 5

1 Nimer thinks that oranges that are very juicy cost more than those that are not very juicy. He buys 20 oranges from different places, and measures the amount of juice (j ml), that each orange produces. He also notes the price (p) of each orange.

The data can be summarised as follows,

$$\sum j = 979 \qquad \sum p = 735 \qquad \sum j^2 = 52\,335 \qquad \sum p^2 = 32\,156 \qquad \sum jp = 39\,950$$

a Find S_{jj}, S_{pp} and S_{jp}. **(3 marks)**

b Using your answers to part **a**, calculate the product moment correlation coefficient. **(1 mark)**

c Describe the type of correlation between the amount of juice and the cost.
State, with a reason, whether or not Nimer is correct. **(2 marks)**

(E)   2   Two judges at a cat show place the 10 entries in the following rank orders.

Cat	A	B	C	D	E	F	G	H	I	J
First judge	4	6	1	2	5	3	10	9	8	7
Second judge	2	9	3	1	7	4	6	8	5	10

   a   Explain why Spearman's rank correlation coefficient is appropriate for these data.   **(1 mark)**

   b   Find the value of Spearman's rank correlation coefficient.   **(3 marks)**

   c   Explain briefly the role of the null and alternative hypotheses in a test of significance. **(1 mark)**

   d   Stating your hypotheses clearly, carry out a test at the 5% level of significance and use
       your result to comment on the extent of the agreement between the two judges.   **(4 marks)**

(E/P)   3   a   Explain briefly the conditions under which you would measure correlation using
           Spearman's rank correlation coefficient.   **(1 mark)**

   b   Nine applicants for places at a college were interviewed by two tutors. Each tutor
       ranked the applicants in order of merit (the quality of being good). The rankings
       are shown below.

Applicant	A	B	C	D	E	F	G	H	I
Tutor 1	1	2	3	4	5	6	7	8	9
Tutor 2	1	3	5	4	2	7	9	8	6

   By carrying out a suitable hypothesis test, investigate the extent of the agreement
   between the two tutors.   **(7 marks)**

(E)   4   In a ski jumping contest, each competitor made two jumps. The order of merit for the
       10 competitors who completed both jumps are shown.

Ski jumper	A	B	C	D	E	F	G	H	I	J
First jump	2	9	7	4	10	8	6	5	1	3
Second jump	4	10	5	1	8	9	2	7	3	6

   a   Calculate, to 2 decimal places, Spearman's rank correlation coefficient for the
       performance of the ski jumpers in the two jumps.   **(3 marks)**

   b   Using a 5% level of significance, and quoting from the table of critical values, investigate
       whether there is a positive association between performance on the first and second jumps.
       State your null and alternative hypotheses clearly.   **(4 marks)**

(E/P)   5   An expert on pottery is asked to place seven china bowls in date order of manufacture,
       assigning the rank 1 to the oldest bowl. The actual dates of manufacture and the order
       given by the expert are shown below.

Bowl	A	B	C	D	E	F	G
Date of manufacture	1920	1857	1710	1896	1810	1690	1780
Order given by expert	7	3	4	6	2	1	5

   Carry out a hypothesis test to determine whether the expert is able to judge relative age
   accurately. You must state:
   • the significance level of your test
   • your null and alternative hypotheses
   • which correlation coefficient, with the reason why.   **(8 marks)**

(E) **6** A bus company provides a service for a small town and some nearby villages. In a study of their service, a random sample of 20 journeys was taken. The distances x, in kilometres, and journey times t, in minutes, were recorded. The average distance was 4.535 km and the average journey time was 15.15 minutes.

    a Using $\sum x^2 = 493.77$, $\sum t^2 = 4897$, $\sum xt = 1433.8$, calculate the product moment correlation coefficient for these data. **(3 marks)**

    b Stating your hypotheses clearly, test, at the 5% level of significance, whether or not there is evidence of a positive correlation between journey time and distance. **(4 marks)**

    c State any assumptions that have to be made to justify the test in part **b**. **(1 mark)**

(E) **7** A group of students scored the following marks in their Statistics and Geography exams.

Student	A	B	C	D	E	F	G	H
Statistics	64	71	49	38	72	55	54	68
Geography	55	50	51	47	65	45	39	82

    a Find the value of Spearman's rank correlation coefficient between the marks of these students. **(3 marks)**

    b Stating your hypotheses and using a 5% level of significance, test whether marks in Statistics and marks in Geography are associated. **(4 marks)**

(E/P) **8** An international study investigated whether there was any correlation between the life expectancy (the number of years an average person is likely to live) of females and the percentage of adult females who were literate (able to read and write). A random sample of 8 countries was taken and the following data were collected.

SKILLS
ADAPTIVE
LEARNING

Life expectancy (years)	49	76	69	71	50	64	78	74
Literacy (%)	25	88	80	62	37	86	89	67

    a Find Spearman's rank correlation coefficient for these data. **(3 marks)**

    b Stating your hypotheses clearly, at the 5% level of significance, test whether or not there is evidence of a correlation between the rankings of literacy and life expectancy for females. **(4 marks)**

    c Give one reason why Spearman's rank correlation coefficient (and not the product moment correlation coefficient) has been used in this case. **(1 mark)**

    d Without recalculating the correlation coefficient, explain how your answer to part **a** would change if:

       i the literacy percentage for the eighth country was actually 77

      ii a ninth country was added to the sample with life expectancy 79 years and literacy percentage 92%. **(3 marks)**

(E) **9** Six sheep were ranked in order of merit at a farm show by the official judge and by a student vet. The ranks were as follows:

Official judge	1	2	3	4	5	6
Student vet	1	5	4	2	6	3

    a Calculate Spearman's rank correlation coefficient between these rankings. **(3 marks)**

b Investigate whether or not there was agreement between the rankings of the judge and the student vet.

State clearly your hypotheses, and carry out an appropriate one-tailed significance test at the 5% level. **(4 marks)**

(E) **10** As part of a survey in a particular profession, age, x years, and salary, €y thousands, were recorded.

The values of x and y for a randomly selected sample of ten members of the profession are given in this table:

x	30	52	38	48	56	44	41	25	32	27
y	22	38	40	34	35	32	28	27	29	41

$\sum x = 393$ $\sum x^2 = 16483$ $\sum y = 326$ $\sum y^2 = 10968$ $\sum xy = 13014$

a Calculate, to 3 decimal places, the product moment correlation coefficient between age and salary. **(3 marks)**

b State two conditions under which it might be appropriate to use Spearman's rank correlation coefficient. **(1 mark)**

c Calculate, to 3 decimal places, Spearman's rank correlation coefficient between age and salary. **(3 marks)**

It is suggested that there is no correlation between age and salary.

d Set up appropriate null and alternative hypotheses and carry out an appropriate test to evaluate this suggestion. Use a 5% significance level. **(4 marks)**

(E) **11** A machine hire company kept records of the age, X months, and the maintenance costs, CAD\$$Y$, of one type of machine. The following table summarises the data for a random sample of 10 machines.

Machine	A	B	C	D	E	F	G	H	I	J
Age, x	63	12	34	81	51	14	45	74	24	89
Maintenance cost, y	111	25	41	181	64	21	51	145	43	241

a Calculate, to 3 decimal places, the product moment correlation coefficient. You may use $\sum x^2 = 30625$ $\sum y^2 = 135481$ $\sum xy = 62412$ **(3 marks)**

b Calculate, to 3 decimal places, Spearman's rank correlation coefficient. **(3 marks)**

For a different type of machine, similar data were collected. From a large population of such machines a random sample of 10 was taken and Spearman's rank correlation coefficient, based on $\sum d^2 = 36$, was 0.782.

c Using a 5% level of significance and quoting from the tables of critical values, interpret this rank correlation coefficient. Use a two-tailed test and state clearly your null and alternative hypotheses. **(4 marks)**

(E) **12** The data below show the height above sea level, x metres, and the temperature, y °C, at 7.00 a.m., on the same day in summer at nine places in Europe.

Height, x (m)	1400	400	280	790	390	590	540	1250	680
Temperature, y (°C)	6	15	18	10	16	14	13	7	13

a Use your calculator to find the product moment correlation coefficient for this sample. **(1 mark)**

b Test, at the 5% significance level, whether height above sea level and temperature are negatively correlated. **(4 marks)**

On the same day, the number of hours of sunshine was recorded and Spearman's rank correlation coefficient between hours of sunshine and temperature, based on $\sum d^2 = 28$, was 0.767

c Stating your hypotheses and using a 5% two-tailed test, interpret this rank correlation coefficient. **(4 marks)**

(E) **13 a** Explain briefly the conditions under which you would measure association using Spearman's rank correlation coefficient rather than the product moment correlation coefficient. **(1 mark)**

At a farm show, 10 sheep were ranked by a qualified judge and by a trainee judge. Their rankings are shown in the table.

Qualified judge	1	2	3	4	5	6	7	8	9	10
Trainee judge	1	2	5	6	7	8	10	4	3	9

b Calculate Spearman's rank correlation coefficient for these data. **(3 marks)**

c Using a suitable table and a 5% significance level, state your conclusions as to whether there is some degree of agreement between the two sets of ranks. **(4 marks)**

(E) **14** The positions in a league table of 8 basketball clubs at the end of a season are shown, together with the average number of spectators (in hundreds) at home matches during the season.

Club	A	B	C	D	E	F	G	H
Position	1	2	3	4	5	6	7	8
Average number of spectators (100s)	30	32	12	19	27	18	15	25

Calculate Spearman's rank correlation coefficient between position in the league and home attendance. Comment on your results. **(4 marks)**

(E/P) **15** The ages, in months, and the weights, in kg, of a random sample of nine babies are shown in the table below.

Baby	A	B	C	D	E	F	G	H	I
Age (x)	1	2	2	3	3	3	4	4	5
Weight (y)	4.4	5.2	5.8	6.4	6.7	7.2	7.6	7.9	8.4

a The product moment correlation coefficient between weight and age for these babies was found to be 0.972. By testing for positive correlation at the 5% significance level, interpret this value. **(4 marks)**

A boy who does not know the weights or ages of these babies is asked to list them, by guessing, in order of increasing weight. He puts them in the order:

     A   C   E   B   G   D   I   F   H

b Obtain, to 3 decimal places, a rank correlation coefficient between the boy's order and the true weight order. **(3 marks)**

c By carrying out a suitable hypothesis test at the 5% significance level, assess the boy's ability to correctly rank the babies by weight. **(4 marks)**

Challenge

x_i and y_i are ranked variables with no ties, so that each takes the values 1, 2, 3, ... n exactly once. The difference for each pair of data values is defined as $d_i = y_i - x_i$.

a Explain why $\sum x_i^2 = \sum y_i^2 = \sum_{r=1}^{n} r^2$, and hence express the quantity in terms of n.

b Explain why $\sqrt{\sum (x_i - \bar{x})^2 \sum (y_i - \bar{y}^2)} = \sum (x_i - \bar{x})^2$, and hence show that $\sqrt{\sum (x_i - \bar{x})^2 \sum (y_i - \bar{y})^2} = \dfrac{n(n^2 - 1)}{12}$

c By expanding $\sum (y_i - x_i)^2$, show that $\sum x_i y_i = \sum x_i^2 - \dfrac{\sum d_i^2}{2}$

d Hence show that $\sum (x_i - x)(y_i - y) = \dfrac{n(n^2 - 1)}{12} - \dfrac{\sum d_i^2}{2}$

e Hence, or otherwise, prove that: $\dfrac{\sum (x_i - \bar{x})(y_i - \bar{y})}{\sqrt{\sum (x_i - \bar{x})^2 \sum (y_i - \bar{y})^2}} = 1 - \dfrac{6 \sum d_i^2}{n(n^2 - 1)}$

Summary of key points

1 The product moment correlation coefficient r is given by $r = \dfrac{S_{xy}}{\sqrt{S_{xx} S_{yy}}}$

2 Spearman's rank correlation coefficient is a special case of the product moment correlation coefficient in which the data are converted to rankings before calculating the coefficient. To rank two sets of data, X and Y, you give rank 1 to the highest of the x_i values, 2 to the next highest and so on. You do the same for the y_i values.

3 A Spearman's rank correlation coefficient of:
   +1 means that rankings are in perfect agreement
   −1 means that the rankings are in exact reverse order
    0 means that there is no correlation between the rankings.

4 If there are no tied ranks, Spearman's rank correlation coefficient r_s is calculated using:

$$r_s = 1 - \dfrac{6 \sum d^2}{n(n^2 - 1)}$$

where d is the difference between the ranks of each observation, and n is the number of pairs of observations.

5 Equal data values should be assigned a rank equal to the mean of the tied ranks and then PMCC calculated.

6 For a one-tailed test, use either:
   - $H_0 : \rho = 0$, $H_1 : \rho > 0$ or
   - $H_0 : \rho = 0$, $H_1 : \rho < 0$

For a two-tailed test, use:
   - $H_0 : \rho = 0$, $H_1 : \rho \neq 0$

6 GOODNESS OF FIT AND CONTINGENCY TABLES

4.1
4.2

Prior knowledge check

1 Given that $X \sim \text{Po}(5)$, find $\text{P}(X < 2)$. ← **Statistics 2 Section 2.1**

2 Given that $X \sim \text{N}(4, 3)$, find $\text{P}(X > 5)$. ← **Statistics 1 Section 7.1**

3 David claims 60% of the students in his school like sweetcorn. He takes a random sample of 100 students and finds that 70 of them say that they like sweetcorn. Test David's claim, at the 5% significance level.
← **Statistics 3 Section 4.4**

The chi-squared test is used in genetics to help determine whether an experiment was fair and unbiased, and to provide a level of confidence for whether the results were obtained by chance.
→ **Exercise 6A, Q4**

6.1 Goodness of fit

Goodness of fit is concerned with measuring how well an observed frequency distribution fits to a known distribution.

If you roll a six-sided dice 120 times, you might get results like these:

Number on dice, n	1	2	3	4	5	6
Observed frequency	23	15	25	18	21	18

If the dice is unbiased you would, in theory, expect each of the numbers 1 to 6 to appear the same number of times.

For 120 rolls, the expected frequencies would each be:

$$P(X = x) \times 120 = \tfrac{1}{6} \times 120 = 20$$

You would expect results like these:

Number on dice, n	1	2	3	4	5	6
Expected frequency	20	20	20	20	20	20

The expected results fit a uniform discrete probability distribution:

x:	1	2	3	4	5	6
$P(X = x)$:	$\tfrac{1}{6}$	$\tfrac{1}{6}$	$\tfrac{1}{6}$	$\tfrac{1}{6}$	$\tfrac{1}{6}$	$\tfrac{1}{6}$

Since you are taking a sample, the observed frequency for each number doesn't match the expected frequency exactly.

If the dice was biased, you would not expect the observed frequency of each number to be exactly 20.

Both the results from the biased and unbiased dice differ from the predicted results, the results from the unbiased dice should be better modelled by the discrete uniform distribution than those from a biased dice.

We create the **hypothesis** that the observed frequency distribution does not differ from a theoretical one, and that any differences are due to natural variations. Because this assumes no difference, it is called the **null hypothesis**.

The **alternative hypothesis** is that the observed frequency distribution does differ from the theoretical one and that any differences are due to not only natural variations but the bias of the dice as well.

- H_0: There is no difference between the observed and the **theoretical distribution**.

- H_1: There is a difference between the observed and the theoretical distribution.

In order to tell how closely the model fits the observed results, you need to have a measure of the goodness of fit between the observed frequencies and the expected frequencies.

This measure used for goodness of fit may be understood by looking further at the results of the dice-rolling experiment.

The results and the frequencies are:

Number on dice, n	1	2	3	4	5	6
Observed frequency, O_i	23	15	25	18	21	18
Expected frequency, E_i	20	20	20	20	20	20

You can show this as a bar chart:

It is easy to see the difference between the observed and the expected values.

To measure the size of these differences, you take the sum of the squares of the differences, divided by the expected frequency:

$$\sum \frac{(O_i - E_i)^2}{E_i} \text{ where:}$$

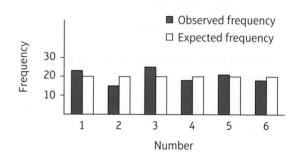

O_i = an observed frequency

E_i = an expected (theoretical) frequency, asserted by the null hypothesis

Each of the $\dfrac{(O_{ij} - E_{ij})^2}{E_{ij}}$ is called a contribution. The larger its value, the more it adds to the test statistic. If, for a particular category it is very high, you may want to investigate the accuracy of the observed data.

This gives a positive number that gets larger as the differences between the observed and the expected frequencies get larger, and smaller as the differences get smaller.

- **The measure of goodness of fit is:**

$$X^2 = \sum_{i=1}^{n} \frac{(O_i - E_i)^2}{E_i}$$

The symbol X^2 is used rather than just X because it shows that the value is never going to be negative.

You can see that the less good the fit, the larger the difference between each observed and expected value, and the greater the value of X^2.

- Another way of calculating X^2 is:

$$X^2 = \sum \frac{(O_i - E_i)^2}{E_i} = \sum \frac{O_i^2 - 2O_iE_i + E_i^2}{E_i}$$

Multiply out the bracket.

$$= \sum \frac{O_i^2}{E_i} - \sum \frac{2O_iE_i}{E_i} + \sum \frac{E_i^2}{E_i}$$

$$= \sum \frac{O_i^2}{E_i} - \sum 2O_i + \sum E_i$$

$$= \sum \frac{O_i^2}{E_i} - \sum O_i$$

$\sum E$ and $\sum O$ are both equal to the total number of trials, or observations. So $\sum E = \sum O = N$.

$$= \sum \frac{O_i^2}{E_i} - N$$

This formula is not given in the formulae booklet, but is easier to use.

Example 1

Bei and Manisha each have two spinners numbered 1–4. They each carry out experiments, where they spin their spinners at the same time, and add the scores together. After each student has carried out 160 experiments, the frequency distributions are as follows:

Number, n	2	3	4	5	6	7	8
Observed by Bei (O_i)	12	15	22	41	33	21	16
Observed by Manisha (O_i)	6	12	21	37	35	29	20
Expected (E_i)	10	20	30	40	30	20	10

Both Bei and Manisha believe that their spinners are fair.

One of the students has a biased spinner.

Calculate the goodness of fit for both students, and determine which of them is most likely to have the biased spinner.

	n	2	3	4	5	6	7	8	Total
Bei	$\dfrac{(O_i - E_i)^2}{E_i}$	0.4	1.25	2.133	0.025	0.3	0.05	3.6	7.755
	$\dfrac{O_i^2}{E_i}$	14.4	11.25	16.133	42.025	36.3	22.05	25.6	167.755
Manisha	$\dfrac{(O_i - E_i)^2}{E_i}$	1.6	3.2	2.7	0.225	0.833	4.05	10	22.608
	$\dfrac{O_i^2}{E_i}$	3.6	7.2	14.7	34.225	40.833	42.05	40	182.608

Results for Bei: $X^2 = \sum\limits_{i=2}^{8} \dfrac{(O_i - E_i)^2}{E_i} = 7.755$ ⟵ Calculate $\sum \dfrac{(O_i - E_i)^2}{E_i}$ or $\sum \dfrac{O_i^2}{E_i} - N$, with $N = 160$.

or using the alternative method:

$X^2 = \sum\limits_{i=2}^{8} \dfrac{O_i^2}{E_i} - N = 167.755 - 160 = 7.755$ ⟵ It is often easier to calculate using the alternative method.

Results for Manisha: $X^2 = \sum\limits_{i=2}^{8} \dfrac{(O_i - E_i)^2}{E_i} = 22.608$

or using the alternative method:

$X^2 = \sum\limits_{i=2}^{8} \dfrac{O_i^2}{E_i} - N = 182.608 - 160 = 22.608$

Manisha's goodness of fit is higher, so she is more likely to have the biased spinner.

Watch out The higher the value of X^2, the **less similar** the observed distribution is to the theoretical distribution.

1 An eight-sided dice is rolled 500 times and the results are noted. It is assumed that the dice is unbiased. A test will show if the observed results differ from the expected ones. Write down a null hypothesis and an alternative hypothesis that can be used.

2 A six-sided dice is rolled 180 times to determine whether or not it is fair.
The results of the rolls are as follows:

Number on dice, n	1	2	3	4	5	6
Observed rolls (O_i)	27	33	31	28	34	27

a State the null and alternative hypotheses for the experiment.

b Calculate X^2 for the observed data.

3 A random sample of 750 school students is taken, and each student's year group is recorded:

Year	7	8	9	10	11
Observed (O_i)	190	145	145	140	130

A researcher wants to find out whether the school students are uniformly distributed across each year group.

a State suitable null and alternative hypotheses.

b Calculate the expected number of students in each year group assuming your null hypothesis is true.

c Calculate X^2 for the observed data.

4 A particular genetic mutation (a change that causes different characteristics) is believed to have a 75% chance of being passed from parent to child. In an experiment, 160 adults with the mutation each had one of their children tested to see if the child had inherited the mutation. The results were as follows:

Mutation present	Yes	No
Observed (O_i)	117	43

a Calculate the expected frequencies.

b State the null and alternative hypotheses.

c Calculate the goodness of fit of the data to the expected result.

(P) **5** Jamal has two coins that he can't tell apart. One is fair. The other is biased and will land on heads with probability 0.6. He flips one of the coins 50 times and records the results in the frequency table given below.

Result	Heads	Tails
Observed (O_i)	28	22

a Calculate the expected frequencies for each coin.

b Calculate the goodness of fit between the observed results and the expected results for each coin.

c Which coin is Jamal more likely to have been using? Give a reason for your answer.

(P) **6** The Body Mass Index profile of English adults is given below.

Country	Underweight	Normal	Overweight	Obese	Total
England	2%	35%	36%	27%	100%

Obesity Statistics, House of Commons Briefing Paper, Number 3336, 2017

You may assume that these percentages reflect the true distribution. A sample is taken of adults in Wales, and the results are recorded in the table below.

Country	Underweight	Normal	Overweight	Obese	Total
Wales (Men)	4	70	80	46	200
Wales (Women)	6	81	65	48	200

By calculating the goodnes of fit statistic for both Welsh men and women, determine which group more closely matches the English distribution.

6.2 Degrees of freedom and the chi-squared (χ^2) family of distributions

An important consideration when deciding goodness of fit is the number of **degrees of freedom**.

Degrees of freedom are calculated from the size of the sample. They are a measure of the amount of information from the sample data that has not been used up. Every time a statistic is calculated from a sample, one degree of freedom is used up.

In order to create a model for the observed frequency distribution, you must use the information about the data in order to select a suitable model. To begin with, you have n observed frequencies, and your model must have the same total frequency as the observed distribution. The requirement that the totals have to agree is called a **constraint**, or **restriction**, and uses up one of your degrees of freedom.

The number of constraints will also depend on the number of parameters needed to describe the distribution and whether or not these parameters are known. If you do not know a parameter, you have to estimate it from the observed data and this uses up a further degree of freedom.

It is usual to refer to each entry of a table that contains an observation as a **cell**. You sometimes have to combine frequencies from different cells of the table. (The reason for this is given on the next page.) If cells are combined in this way then there are fewer expected values. Therefore, when you calculate the number of degrees of freedom you have to count the number of cells after any such combination and subtract the number of constraints from this.

Problem-solving

If you flip a coin 100 times and observe the results, there are **two observed frequencies**: the number of heads, and the number of tails. There is **one constraint**: the fact that the total frequency must be 100. Therefore the number of degrees of freedom is $2 - 1 = 1$. If you know one frequency, x, then you can calculate the other, $100 - x$. If a dice is rolled 120 times, there are **six observed frequencies** and **one constraint** (the total number of rolls). There are $6 - 1 = 5$ degrees of freedom. Setting values for any 5 of the frequencies uniquely determines the 6th. **→ Section 6.4**

Watch out If the estimate of a parameter is calculated then it is a restriction. If it is guessed by using an estimate from observations then it is not a restriction.

■ $\dfrac{\text{Number of}}{\text{degrees of freedom}} = \dfrac{\text{Number of cells}}{\text{(after any combining)}} - \text{Number of constraints}$

The χ^2 (pronounced kye-squared) family of distributions can be used as approximations for the statistic X^2. We write this:

● $X^2 = \sum \dfrac{(O_i - E_i)^2}{E_i} = \sum \dfrac{O_i^2}{E_i} - N \sim \chi^2$

X^2 is approximated well by χ^2 as long as none of the expected values (E_i) fall below 5.

■ **If any of the expected values are less than 5, then you have to combine expected frequencies in the data table until they are greater than 5.**

Usually frequencies next to each other in the table are joined together because if one value is low, the next one is also likely to be low.

The χ^2 family of distributions are theoretical ones. The probability distribution function of each member of the family depends on the number of degrees of freedom.

Notation

The number of degrees of freedom in a χ^2 distribution is written using the Greek letter ν, which is pronounced 'nu'.

To show which member of the family of distributions you are talking about, you write χ^2_ν. Thus χ^2_4 is the χ^2 distribution with $\nu = 4$.

■ **When selecting which member of the χ^2 family to use as an approximation for X^2, you select the distribution which has ν equal to the number of degrees of freedom of your expected values.**

Example **2**   **SKILLS** ▷ **DECISION MAKING**

In a sample of 100 households, the expected number of pet fish is as follows:

Fish	0	1	2	3	4	5	>5	Total
Expected	55	20	10	7	4	3	1	100

Select an appropriate **chi-squared distribution** to model the goodness of fit X^2 for these data.

χ^2 is a good approximation for X^2 only if none of the expected values are less than 5, so we combine the expected values for 4, 5 and >5 fish into a single value.

Combining the frequencies:

Fish	0	1	2	3	>3	Total
Expected	55	20	10	7	8	100

Degrees of freedom = 5 − 1 = 4

Therefore $X^2 \sim \chi^2_4$ is the correct approximation.

There are 5 values. You know the total of the frequencies must be 100 so there is one constraint.

We can perform a hypothesis test with the question: 'Could the value of $X^2 = \sum \dfrac{(O_i - E_i)^2}{E_i}$ calculated for your sample come from a population for which X^2 is equal to zero?'

As with all hypothesis tests, you will reject the null hypothesis only if you have only a small chance of being wrong. Typically this figure is a probability of 5%.

To find the value of X^2 that is only exceeded with probability of 5% (the critical value), we use the appropriate χ^2 distribution.

Notation For a given value of ν, the critical value of χ^2 which is exceeded with probability 5% is written χ^2_ν (5%) or χ^2_ν (0.05).

Example 3

Look across the table to get column 0.050.

With $\nu = 5$, find the value of χ^2 that is exceeded with 0.05 probability.

Look down the table to get row $\nu = 5$.

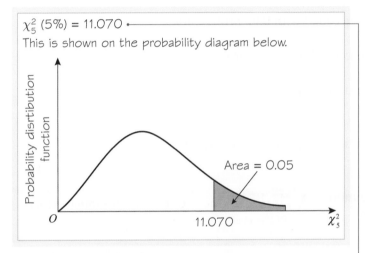

χ^2_5 (5%) = 11.070
This is shown on the probability diagram below.

Area = 0.05

11.070

Use the table of values on page 142 for the percentage points of the χ^2 distribution, with $\nu = 5$.

ν	0.995	0.100	0.050	0.025
1	0.000	2.705	3.841	5.024
2	0.010	4.605	5.991	7.378
3	0.072	6.251	7.815	9.348
4	0.207	7.779	9.488	11.143
5	0.412	9.236	11.070	12.832
6	0.676	0.645	12.592	14.449
7	0.989	2.017	14.067	16.013

Read off where row and column cross: the value is 11.070.

Also from the table, χ^2_5 (10%) = 9.236 and χ^2_5 (2.5%) = 12.832.
For each other value of ν, the critical values may be looked up in the same way.

You can also find values for χ^2 distributions on some graphical calculators.

Example 4 **SKILLS** PROBLEM-SOLVING

a Find the following critical values:
  i χ^2_3 (95%)   **ii** χ^2_4 (10%)
b Find the smallest values of y such that:
  i $P(\chi^2_2 > y) = 0.95$ **ii** $P(\chi^2_4 > y) = 0.99$

Online Explore the χ^2-squared distribution and use it to determine critical values for goodness of fit using GeoGebra.

a i $\nu = 3$
   Level of significance = 0.95
   From the table on page 142, the critical value of χ^2 is 0.352

ii $\nu = 4$
   Level of significance = 0.1
   From the table on page 142, the critical value of χ^2 is 7.779

b i $P(\chi^2_2 > 0.103) = 95\%$

ii $P(\chi^2_4 > 0.297) = 99\%$

The significance level is the probability that the distribution exceeds the critical value.
χ^2_2 (95%) = 0.103
so $P(\chi^2_2 > 0.103) = 95\%$

Exercise 6B

1 A group of 50 students record the days (Monday–Sunday) that their birthdays will fall on this year. How many degrees of freedom are there in the frequency distribution?

2 For 5 degrees of freedom, find the critical value of χ^2 which is exceeded with a probability of 5%.

3 Find the following critical values:

   a $\chi_5^2 \,(5\%)$ **b** $\chi_8^2 \,(1\%)$ **c** $\chi_{10}^2 \,(10\%)$

4 With $\nu = 10$, find the value of χ^2 that is exceeded with 0.05 probability.

5 With $\nu = 8$, find the value of χ^2 that is exceeded with 0.10 probability.

6 The random variable Y has a χ^2 distribution with 8 degrees of freedom. Find y such that $P(Y > y) = 0.99$

7 The random variable X has a χ^2 distribution with 5 degrees of freedom. Find x such that $P(X > x) = 0.95$

(P) 8 The random variable Y has a χ^2 distribution with 12 degrees of freedom.

   Find:

   a y such that $P(Y < y) = 0.05$

   b y such that $P(Y < y) = 0.95$.

Notation The χ^2 distribution is continuous, so $P(Y < y) = 1 - P(Y > y)$.

6.3 Testing a hypothesis

By using a suitable χ^2 distribution to model the goodness of fit, you can carry out a **hypothesis test** for the null hypothesis that the observed data fits the theoretical distribution.

Notation α is used to denote the significance level to which the data is being tested.

You need to choose a significance level α for the hypothesis test. This is often 5%, and will be given in the question.

You can then calculate the critical value $\chi_\nu^2(\alpha)$ which will depend on the significance level α and the number of degrees of freedom ν. The probability of observing data with a goodness of fit exceeding the critical value is α.

- If X^2 exceeds the critical value, it is unlikely that the null hypothesis is correct, so you reject it.

Watch out A hypothesis test for goodness of fit is always **one-tailed**. This means the **critical region** is always the set of values **greater than** the critical value.

Example 5   **SKILLS** REASONING/ARGUMENTATION

In an experiment where a six-sided dice is rolled 120 times, the frequency distribution is to be compared to a discrete uniform distribution as shown:

Number on dice, n	1	2	3	4	5	6
Observed frequency, O_i	23	15	25	18	21	18
Expected frequency, E_i	20	20	20	20	20	20

Test, at the 5% significance level, whether or not the observed frequencies could be modelled by a discrete uniform distribution.

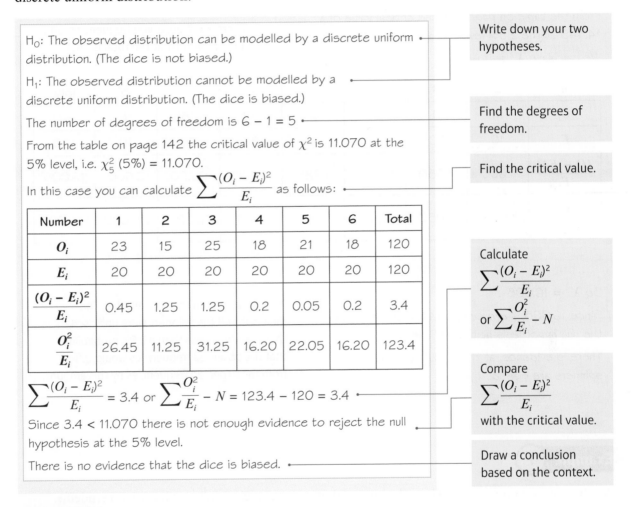

H_0: The observed distribution can be modelled by a discrete uniform distribution. (The dice is not biased.)

H_1: The observed distribution cannot be modelled by a discrete uniform distribution. (The dice is biased.)

Write down your two hypotheses.

The number of degrees of freedom is $6 - 1 = 5$

Find the degrees of freedom.

From the table on page 142 the critical value of χ^2 is 11.070 at the 5% level, i.e. χ_5^2 (5%) = 11.070.

Find the critical value.

In this case you can calculate $\sum \dfrac{(O_i - E_i)^2}{E_i}$ as follows:

Number	1	2	3	4	5	6	Total
O_i	23	15	25	18	21	18	120
E_i	20	20	20	20	20	20	120
$\dfrac{(O_i - E_i)^2}{E_i}$	0.45	1.25	1.25	0.2	0.05	0.2	3.4
$\dfrac{O_i^2}{E_i}$	26.45	11.25	31.25	16.20	22.05	16.20	123.4

Calculate
$$\sum \dfrac{(O_i - E_i)^2}{E_i}$$
or $\sum \dfrac{O_i^2}{E_i} - N$

$$\sum \dfrac{(O_i - E_i)^2}{E_i} = 3.4 \text{ or } \sum \dfrac{O_i^2}{E_i} - N = 123.4 - 120 = 3.4$$

Since 3.4 < 11.070 there is not enough evidence to reject the null hypothesis at the 5% level.

Compare
$$\sum \dfrac{(O_i - E_i)^2}{E_i}$$
with the critical value.

There is no evidence that the dice is biased.

Draw a conclusion based on the context.

Example 6

Alan has two identical spinners with the numbers 1–4 written on each of them. He carries out experiments, where he spins both of his spinners at the same time and adds the scores together. After 160 experiments, the frequency distribution is as follows:

Number, n	2	3	4	5	6	7	8
Observed by Alan (O_i)	14	11	26	33	42	18	16
Expected (E_i)	10	20	30	40	30	20	10

The table also shows the expected distribution of the scores if both spinners are unbiased.

Test, at the 2.5% significance level, whether the observed frequencies could be modelled by the expected distribution shown.

H_0: The observed distribution can be modelled by the expected distribution shown. (The spinners are not biased.)

H_1: The observed distribution cannot be modelled by the expected distribution shown. (The spinners are biased.)

The number of degrees of freedom is $7 - 1 = 6$

From the table on page 142, the critical value of χ^2 is 14.449 at the 2.5% level, i.e. $\chi^2_6(2.5\%) = 14.449$

We calculate X^2 as follows:

> The null hypothesis is what we believe unless the evidence suggests otherwise. In this case, we assume the spinners are equally likely to land on any number.

> There are 7 observed frequencies, and 1 constraint (that the total is 160).

n	2	3	4	5	6	7	8	Total
O_i	14	11	26	33	42	18	16	160
E_i	10	20	30	40	30	20	10	160
$\dfrac{(O_i - E_i)^2}{E_i}$	1.600	4.050	0.533	1.225	4.800	0.200	3.600	16.008
$\dfrac{O_i^2}{E_i}$	19.600	6.050	22.533	27.225	58.800	16.200	25.600	176.008

So $X^2 = 16.008$

Since 16.008 is greater than 14.449, we reject the null hypothesis at the 2.5% level.

There is evidence, at the 2.5% level, that the spinners are biased.

> X^2 is greater than the critical value. This means that if the spinners were unbiased, there would be less than a 2.5% probability that the observed frequencies would differ from the expected frequencies by this amount.

Example 7

A school carried out a survey into the impact that a new exercise club was having on students. Before the new club started, 60% of students said they did no regular exercise, 30% reported exercising once a week and 10% reported exercising more than once a week. After the new club started, the 150 students were surveyed to find out how often they exercised.

	No regular exercise	Once a week	More than once a week	Total
Frequency	73	57	20	150

Based on these data, is there evidence of a change in attitude to exercise following the introduction of the new club? Test the data at a 5% significance level.

H_0: The observed distribution has not changed from the original distribution

H_1: The observed distribution has changed from the original distribution.

The number of degrees of freedom is $3 - 1 = 2$

From the table on page 142, the critical value of χ^2 is 5.991 at the 5% level, i.e. $\chi_2^2(5\%) = 5.991$.

We calculate X^2 as follows:

	No exercise	Once a week	More than once a week	Total
Observed	73	57	20	150
Expected	$0.6 \times 150 = 90$	$0.3 \times 150 = 45$	$0.1 \times 150 = 15$	150
$\dfrac{(O_i - E_i)^2}{E_i}$	3.211	3.200	1.667	8.078
$\dfrac{O_i^2}{E_i}$	59.211	72.200	26.667	158.078

So $X^2 = 8.078$

Since 8.078 is greater than 5.991, we reject the null hypothesis at the 5% significance level.

Therefore, at the 5% significance level, there is evidence that the observed distribution has changed from the original distribution. The new club has had an effect on the number of times students exercise each week.

There are 3 observed frequencies, and 1 constraint, so 2 degrees of freedom.

The expected values are based on the proportions before the club was started.

Watch out A test for goodness of fit only tells you how closely the observed data matches the theoretical (or assumed) distribution. You cannot conclude that the new club has increased the amount of exercise students do – only that the amount has changed.

Exercise 6C **SKILLS** REASONING/ARGUMENTATION

(E) **1** In an experiment where a dice is rolled 72 times, the frequency distribution is to be compared to a discrete uniform distribution as shown:

Number on dice, n	1	2	3	4	5	6
Observed frequency, O_i	16	11	13	15	8	9
Expected frequency, E_i	12	12	12	12	12	12

Test, at the 5% significance level, whether or not the observed frequencies could be modelled by a discrete uniform distribution. **(6 marks)**

(E) **2** In a bag, the ratio of red balls to gray balls is 1 : 4.
120 people, with replacement, select a ball from the bag.

	Red	Gray	Total
Observed colour	15	105	120

Test, at the 5% significance level, whether or not the ratio of red to gray is correct. **(6 marks)**

(E) 3 A local travel agent has predicted how many trips abroad his customers make.
He surveys a sample of 100 customers and compares the results to his expectations.

Trips abroad	None	One	Two or more
Expected	10%	60%	30%
Sample	4	73	23

Test, at the 2.5% significance level, whether the travel agent's prediction fits the observed data.

(6 marks)

(E/P) 4 In a sample of 100 households, the actual and expected numbers
of cats is as follows:

Cats	0	1	2	3	4	5	>5	Total
Observed	45	19	11	8	7	6	4	100
Expected	55	20	10	7	4	3	1	100

Problem-solving

When using a χ^2 distribution
to approximate the
distribution of X^2, if any of
the expected frequencies
are less than 5 you need to
combine cells.

a Explain why there are 4 degrees of freedom in
this case. **(2 marks)**

b Test, at the 5% significance level, whether the observed data
fits the expected distribution given. **(5 marks)**

(E/P) 5 In the year 2000, the birth weights of babies were distributed as follows:

Weight (g)	Under 1500	1500–1999	2000–2499	2500–2999	3000–3499	3500 and over	Total
Percentage	1.3%	1.5%	5%	16.5%	35.7%	40%	100%

In the year 2015, the birth weights of babies were as follows:

Weight (g)	Under 1500	1500–1999	2000–2499	2500–2999	3000–3499	3500 and over	Total
Frequency	7286	9304	32 121	112 535	244 472	281 942	687 660

Using a 5% significance level, decide whether the distribution of birth weights from 2000
can be used as a model for the weights in 2015. **(8 marks)**

6.4 Testing the goodness of fit with discrete data

The steps for testing goodness of fit with discrete data can be summarised as follows.

1 Determine which distribution is likely to be a good model by
examining the conditions applying to the observed data.

> These will usually be
> given in the question.

2 Set the significance level, for example, 5%.

3 Estimate parameters (if necessary) from your observed data.

4 Form your hypotheses.

5 Calculate expected frequencies.

6 Combine any expected frequencies so that none are less than 5.

7 Find ν using ν = number of cells after combining – number of constraints or restrictions.

8 Find the critical value of χ^2 from the table.

9 Calculate $\sum \dfrac{(O_i - E_i)^2}{E_i}$ or $\sum \dfrac{O_i^2}{E_i} - N$

10 See if your value is significant.

11 Draw the appropriate conclusion and interpret in the context of the original problem.

Testing a discrete uniform distribution as a model

You have already seen an example of this. The conditions under which a discrete uniform distribution arises are:

- the discrete random variable X is defined over a set of k distinct (separate) values
- each value is equally likely

The probability of each value is given by

$$P(X = x_r) = \frac{1}{k} \qquad r = 1, 2, \dots, k$$

The frequencies for a sample size of N are given by

$$\text{Frequency} = P(X = x_r) \times N = \frac{1}{k} \times N \qquad r = 1, 2, \dots, k$$

In a discrete uniform distribution, the probability of each outcome is dependent only on the size of the sample space. This means that there are no additional parameters to estimate, so the only restriction is that the expected frequencies add up to N. The number of degrees of freedom is **one less** than the number of cells, after any cells have been combined.

Example 8

100 digits between 0 and 9 are selected from a table with the frequencies as shown below.

Digit	0	1	2	3	4	5	6	7	8	9
Frequency	11	8	8	7	8	9	12	9	13	15

Could the digits be from a random number table? Test at the 5% significance level.

Each digit should have an equal chance of selection, so the appropriate model is the discrete uniform distribution.

H_0: A discrete uniform distribution is a suitable model.
(The digits are random.)

H_1: A discrete uniform distribution is not a suitable model.
(The digits are not random.)

$$P(X = x_r) = \tfrac{1}{10} \qquad r = 0, 1, \dots, 9$$

The number of degrees of freedom is:

$$\nu = 10 - 1 = 9$$

Determine the distribution. The significance level is given as 5% and no parameters need estimating.

State your hypotheses.

Find ν.

From the table on page 142, χ_9^2 (5%) = 16.919 — **Find the critical value.**

Digit	0	1	2	3	4	5	6	7	8	9
Observed, O_i	11	8	8	7	8	9	12	9	13	15
Expected, E_i	10	10	10	10	10	10	10	10	10	10
$\dfrac{(O_i - E_i)^2}{E_i}$	0.1	0.4	0.4	0.9	0.4	0.1	0.4	0.1	0.9	2.5

Calculate $\sum \dfrac{(O_i - E_i)^2}{E_i}$ **or** $\sum \dfrac{O_i^2}{E_i} - N.$

$$\sum \frac{(O_i - E_i)^2}{E_i} = 6.2$$

So: $$\sum \frac{(O_i - E_i)^2}{E_i} < 16.919$$

See if your value is significant.

Do not reject H_0: there is no evidence to suggest the digits are not random.

Draw a conclusion in the context of the original problem.

Testing a binomial distribution as a model

The conditions under which a binomial distribution arises are:

- there must be a fixed number (n) of trials in each observation
- the trials must be independent
- the trials have only two outcomes: success and failure
- the probability of success (p) is constant

For a binomial random variable:

$$P(X = r) = \binom{n}{r} p^r (1 - p)^{n-r} \qquad r = 0, 1, 2, \ldots, n$$

The frequency f_r with which each r occurs when the number of observations is N is given by

$$f_r = P(X = r) \times N$$

The binomial distribution has two parameters, n and p. You have the usual restriction that the expected frequencies must have the same total as observed frequencies, while p may be known or it may be estimated from the observed values by using frequencies of success.

$$p = \frac{\text{total number of successes}}{\text{number of trials} \times N} = \frac{\Sigma(r \times f_r)}{n \times N}$$

If p is not estimated by calculation: ν = number of cells − 1
If p is estimated by calculation: ν = number of cells − 2

Watch out For a binomial distribution, each observation is of the number of successes in n trials. So for N observations there are $n \times N$ trials in total.

Example **9** **SKILLS** REASONING/ARGUMENTATION

The data in the table are thought to be modelled by a binomial distribution B(10, 0.2). Use the table for the binomial **cumulative** distribution function to find expected values, and conduct a test to see if this is a good model. Use a 5% significance level.

x	0	1	2	3	4	5	6	7	8
Frequency	12	28	28	17	7	4	2	2	0

H_0: A B(10, 0.2) distribution is a suitable model for the results.

H_1: The results cannot be modelled by a B(10, 0.2) distribution.

> State your hypotheses.

We can use the cumulative binomial tables for $n = 10$ to find the probabilities.

$p =$	0.05	0.10	0.15	0.20	0.25
$n = 10, x = 0$	0.5987	0.3487	0.1969	0.1074	0.0563
1	0.9139	0.7361	0.5443	0.3758	0.2440
2	0.9885	0.9298	0.8202	0.6778	0.5256
3	0.9990	0.9872	0.9500	0.8791	0.7759
4	0.9999	0.9984	0.9901	0.9672	00.9219
5	1.0000	0.9999	0.9986	0.9936	0.9803
6	1.0000	1.0000	0.9999	0.9991	0.9965
7	1.0000	1.0000	1.0000	0.9999	0.9996
8	1.0000	1.0000	1.0000	1.0000	1.0000
9	1.0000	1.0000	1.0000	1.0000	1.0000

x	0	1	2	3	4	5	6	7	8
Probability of x	0.1074	0.2684	0.3020	0.2013	0.0881	0.0264	0.0055	0.0008	0.0001
Expected frequencies	10.74	26.84	30.20	20.13	8.81	2.64	0.55	0.08	0.01

There are $7 + 4 + 2 + 2 = 15$ observed values when $x \geqslant 4$.

Expected frequency $= 8.81 + 2.64 + 0.55 + 0.08 + 0.01 = 12.09$

> Combine any expected frequencies < 5. (You will have to combine the last five cells in the table since 2.64 + 0.55 + 0.08 + 0.01 < 5.)

x	0	1	2	3	$\geqslant 4$
O_i	12	28	28	17	15
E_i	10.74	26.84	30.20	20.13	12.09
$\dfrac{(O_i - E_i)^2}{E_i}$	0.1478	0.0501	0.1603	0.4867	0.7004

> Find the number of degrees of freedom.

Number of degrees of freedom = number of cells − 1 = 5 − 1 = 4.

(p was not estimated by calculation this time.)

From the table on page 142 the critical value χ_4^2 (5%) is 9.488

> Find the critical value.

$$\sum \frac{(O_i - E_i)^2}{E_i} = 1.5453$$

> Calculate $\sum \dfrac{(O_i - E_i)^2}{E_i}$ or $\sum \dfrac{O_i^2}{E_i} - N.$

$1.545 < 9.488$

> See if the value is significant.

Do not reject H_0: Therefore B(10, 0.2) is a possible model for the data.

> Draw a conclusion.

Example 10   **SKILLS**   REASONING/ARGUMENTATION

A study of the number of girls in families with five children was done on 100 such families. The results are summarised in the following table.

Number of girls (r)	0	1	2	3	4	5
Frequency (f)	13	18	38	20	10	1

It is suggested that the distribution may be modelled by a binomial distribution with $p = 0.5$

a Give reasons why this might be so.

b Test, at the 5% significance level, whether or not a binomial distribution is a good model.

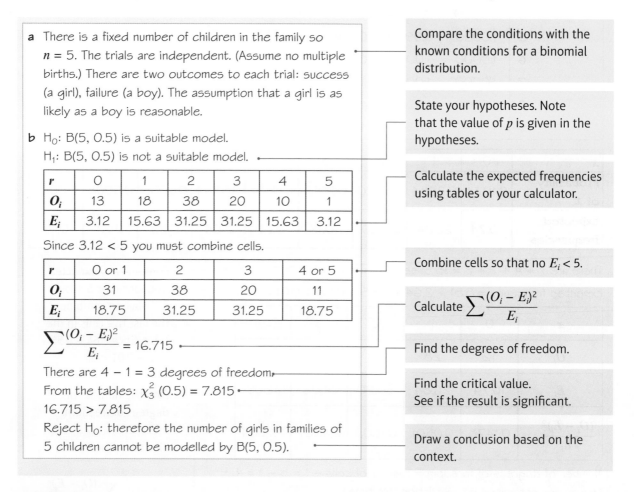

a There is a fixed number of children in the family so $n = 5$. The trials are independent. (Assume no multiple births.) There are two outcomes to each trial: success (a girl), failure (a boy). There are two outcomes to each trial: success (a girl), failure (a boy). The assumption that a girl is as likely as a boy is reasonable.

Compare the conditions with the known conditions for a binomial distribution.

b H_0: B(5, 0.5) is a suitable model.
H_1: B(5, 0.5) is not a suitable model.

State your hypotheses. Note that the value of p is given in the hypotheses.

r	0	1	2	3	4	5
O_i	13	18	38	20	10	1
E_i	3.12	15.63	31.25	31.25	15.63	3.12

Calculate the expected frequencies using tables or your calculator.

Since $3.12 < 5$ you must combine cells.

r	0 or 1	2	3	4 or 5
O_i	31	38	20	11
E_i	18.75	31.25	31.25	18.75

Combine cells so that no $E_i < 5$.

$$\sum \frac{(O_i - E_i)^2}{E_i} = 16.715$$

Calculate $\sum \frac{(O_i - E_i)^2}{E_i}$

There are $4 - 1 = 3$ degrees of freedom.

Find the degrees of freedom.

From the tables: $\chi^2_3 (0.5) = 7.815$

$16.715 > 7.815$

Find the critical value. See if the result is significant.

Reject H_0: therefore the number of girls in families of 5 children cannot be modelled by B(5, 0.5).

Draw a conclusion based on the context.

Example 11

Look at the data in the previous example. By estimating a suitable value of the parameter p, carry out a test, at the 5% significance level, to determine whether a binomial distribution is a suitable model for the data.

Problem-solving

In the previous example you determined that B(5, 0.5) was not a suitable model for the data, at the 5% level. However, B(5, p) may be a suitable model for some different value of p.

H_0: A binomial distribution is a suitable model.

H_1: A binomial distribution is not a suitable model.

State your hypotheses. Since we do not know the parameter p, we cannot include it in our hypotheses.

The number of observations $N = 100$, the number of trials $n = 5$.

$$p = \frac{\Sigma(r \times f_r)}{100n} = \frac{199}{100 \times 5} = 0.398$$

Estimate p.

and, because you estimated p, there will be two constraints.

r	$P(r)$	E_i
0	$(0.602)^5 = 0.0791$	7.91
1	$5(0.602)^4(0.398) = 0.2614$	26.14
2	$10(0.602)^3(0.398)^2 = 0.3456$	34.56
3	$10(0.602)(0.398)^4 = 0.2285$	22.85
4	$5(0.602)^1(0.398)^4 = 0.0755$	7.55
5	$(0.398)^5 = 0.0099$	0.99

Calculate the probabilities using your calculator or the formula for a binomial probability.

r	O_i	E_i	$\dfrac{O_i^2}{E_i}$
0	13	7.91	21.37
1	18	26.14	12.39
2	38	34.56	41.78
3	20	22.85	17.51
>3	11	8.54	14.17
Total			107.22

Combine cells if $E_i < 5$.

Calculate the degrees of freedom.

Find the critical value.

There are $5 - 2 = 3$ degrees of freedom.

The critical value is $\chi_3^2 = 7.815$

$$\sum \frac{(O_i)^2}{E_i} - N = 107.22 - 100 = 7.22$$

Calculate $\sum \dfrac{O_i^2}{E_i} - N$ or $\sum \dfrac{(O_i - E_i)^2}{E_i}$

$7.22 < 7.815$

See if your value is significant.

Do not reject H_0. A binomial distribution is a suitable model.

Draw a conclusion.

Testing a Poisson distribution as a model

The conditions under which a Poisson distribution is likely to arise are:

- the events occur independently of each other
- the events occur singly and at random in continuous space or time
- the events occur at a constant rate, in the sense that the mean number in an interval is proportional to the length of the interval
- the mean and the variance are equal

For a Poisson distribution with mean λ:

$$P(X = r) = \frac{e^{-\lambda}\lambda^r}{r!} \qquad r = 0, 1, 2, \ldots$$

Since the Poisson distribution has an infinite number of integer values, we group all of the larger values together based on our largest observed frequency using: $P(X \geq n) = 1 - P(X \leq n - 1)$

You choose n equal to the highest value of r for which the observed frequency is > 0.
In Example 12, n is chosen to be 7 since all telephone calls for $r \geq 8$ have zero frequencies.

The frequency f_r with which each r occurs is given by $P(X = r) \times N$.

The Poisson distribution has a single parameter λ, which may be known or which may be estimated from the observed data using:

$$\lambda = \frac{\Sigma(r \times f_r)}{N}$$

There is the usual restriction on the total of the expected frequencies being equal to the total of the observed frequencies.

If λ is not estimated by calculation: $\nu = $ number of cells $- 1$
If λ is estimated by calculation: $\nu = $ number of cells $- 2$

Example (12)   **SKILLS**   REASONING/ARGUMENTATION

The numbers of telephone calls arriving at an exchange in six-minute periods were recorded over a period of 8 hours, with the following results.

Number of calls, r	0	1	2	3	4	5	6	7	8
Frequency, f_r	8	19	26	13	7	5	1	1	0

Can these results be modelled by a Poisson distribution? Test at the 5% significance level.

H_0: A Poisson distribution $Po(\lambda)$ is a suitable model.

H_1: The calls cannot be modelled by a Poisson distribution.

Total number of observations $= N = \dfrac{8 \times 60}{6}$

$= 80$

$\lambda = \dfrac{\Sigma(r \times f_r)}{N} = \dfrac{176}{80} = 2.2$

r	$P(X = r)$	Expected frequency of r
0	0.1108	8.864 (0.1108 × 80)
1	0.2438	19.504
2	0.2681	21.448
3	0.1966	15.728
4	0.1082	8.656

You do not know the value of λ so you must estimate it from the observed frequencies.

Use the Poisson distribution function on your calculator, or the formula for a Poisson probability, to calculate the probabilities and expected frequencies for each value of r.

$\lambda = 2.2$ is not in the table so you must calculate the expected frequencies.

Hint   Poisson probabilities can also be calculated from the one before it using

$$P(X = r + 1) = \frac{\lambda \times P(X = r)}{r + 1}$$

r	$P(X = r)$	Expected frequency of r
5	0.0476	3.808
6	0.0174	1.392
7 or more	0.0075	0.6

The value for P(r = 7 or more) is obtained by subtracting the sum of the other probabilities from 1.

r	O_i	E_i	$\dfrac{(O_i - E_i)^2}{E_i}$
0	8	8.864	0.0842
1	19	19.504	0.0130
2	26	21.448	0.9661
3	13	15.728	0.4732
4	7	8.656	0.3168
5 or more	7	5.8	0.2483

$$\sum \frac{(O_i - E_i)^2}{E_i} = 2.1016$$

You have 6 − 2 = 4 degrees of freedom.

From the table on page 192, χ_4^2 (5%) = 9.488

$\qquad$ 2.1016 < 9.488

There is not enough evidence to reject H_o. The calls may be modelled by a Poisson distribution.

In this case, you have to combine cells to give expected frequencies of more than 5.

Since λ was estimated from the observed frequencies there are 2 constraints.

See if your value is significant.

Draw a conclusion.

Exercise **6D**   **SKILLS**   REASONING/ARGUMENTATION

1 The following table shows observed values for a distribution which it is thought may be modelled by a Poisson distribution.

x	0	1	2	3	4	5	>5
Frequency of x	12	23	24	24	12	5	0

A possible model is thought to be Po(2). From tables, the expected values are found to be as shown in the following table.

x	0	1	2	3	4	5	>5
Expected frequency of x	13.53	27.07	27.07	18.04	9.02	3.61	1.66

a Conduct a goodness of fit test at the 5% significance level.

b It is suggested that the model could be improved by estimating the value of λ from the observed results. What effect would this have on the number of constraints placed upon the degrees of freedom?

2 A company receives parcels every day through the mail.

They think that their deliveries are uniformly distributed throughout the week. Test this assertion, given that their deliveries over a four-week period were as follows. Use a 5% significance level.

Day	Mon	Tues	Wed	Thurs	Fri	Sat
Frequency	15	23	19	20	14	11

(P) **3** Over a period of 50 weeks, the numbers of road accidents reported to a police station were as shown.

Number of accidents	0	1	2	3	4
Number of weeks	15	13	9	13	0

a Find the mean number of accidents per week.

b Using this mean and a 10% significance level, test the assertion that these data are from a population with a Poisson distribution.

(P) **4** An archer fires 6 arrows at a target and records the number r of bullseye hits. After a series of 100 such trials he analyses his scores, the frequencies being as follows.

r	0	1	2	3	4	5	6
Frequency	0	26	36	20	10	6	2

a Estimate the probability of hitting a bullseye.

b Use a test at the 5% significance level to see if these results are consistent with the assumption of a binomial distribution.

(E) **5** The table below shows the numbers of employees, in thousands, at five factories and the numbers of accidents in 3 years.

Factory	A	B	C	D	E
Employees (thousands)	4	3	5	1	2
Accidents	22	14	25	8	12

Using a 5% significance level, test the hypothesis that the number of accidents per 1000 employees is constant at each factory. **(6 marks)**

(E/P) **6** In a test to determine the red blood cell count in a patient's blood sample, the number of cells in each of 80 squares is counted with the following results.

Number of cells per square, x	0	1	2	3	4	5	6	7	8
Frequency, f	2	8	15	18	14	13	7	3	0

It is assumed that these will fit a Poisson distribution. Test this assertion at the 5% significance level. **(10 marks)**

(E/P) **7** A factory has a machine. The number of times it broke down each week was recorded over 100 weeks with the following results.

Number of times broken down	0	1	2	3	4	5
Frequency	50	24	12	9	5	0

It is thought that the distribution is Poisson.

a Give reasons why this assumption might be made.   **(2 marks)**

b Test at the 5% significance level to see if the assumption is reasonable.   **(8 marks)**

(E) **8** Data were collected on the numbers of female puppies born in 200 litters of 8 puppies. It was decided to test whether or not a binomial model with parameters $n = 8$ and $p = 0.5$ is a suitable model for the data. The following table shows the observed frequencies and the expected frequencies, to 2 decimal places, obtained in order to carry out this test.

Number of females	Observed number of litters	Expected number of litters
0	1	0.78
1	9	6.25
2	27	21.88
3	46	R
4	49	S
5	35	T
6	26	21.88
7	5	6.25
8	2	0.78

a Find the values of R, S and T.   **(3 marks)**

b Carry out the test to determine whether or not this binomial model is a suitable one. State your hypotheses clearly and use a 5% level of significance.   **(5 marks)**

An alternative test might have involved estimating p rather than assuming $p = 0.5$

c Explain how this would have affected the test.   **(2 marks)**

(E) **9** A random sample of 300 football matches was taken and the numbers of goals scored in each match was recorded. The results are given in the table below.

Number of goals	0	1	2	3	4	5	6	7
Frequency	33	55	80	56	56	11	5	4

a Show that an estimate of the mean number of goals scored in a football match is 2.4 and find an estimate of the variance.   **(3 marks)**

It is thought that a Poisson distribution might provide a good model for the number of goals per match.

b Give one reason why the observed data might support this model.   **(1 mark)**

Using a Poisson distribution, with mean 2.4, expected frequencies were calculated as follows:

Number of goals	0	1	2	3	4	5	6	7
Expected frequency	s	65.3	t	62.7	37.6	18.1	7.2	2.5

c Find the values of s and t.   **(2 marks)**

d State clearly the hypotheses required to test whether or not a Poisson distribution provides a suitable model for these data.   **(1 mark)**

In order to carry out this test, the **class** for 7 goals is redefined as 7 or more goals.

e Find the expected frequency for this class.   **(1 mark)**

The test statistic for the test in part **d** is 15.7 and the number of degrees of freedom used is 5.

f Explain fully why there are 5 degrees of freedom. **(1 mark)**

g Stating clearly the critical value used, carry out the test in part **d** using a 5% level of significance. **(3 marks)**

(E) **10** A biology student believed that a certain species of wild orchid plants grow in random positions in a field. He recorded the number of plants in one square metre of the field, and repeated the procedure to obtain the 148 results in the table.

Number of plants	0	1	2	3	4	5	6	7 or greater
Frequency	9	24	43	34	21	15	2	0

a Show that, to 2 decimal places, the mean number of plants in one square metre is 2.59. **(2 marks)**

b Give a reason why the Poisson distribution might be an appropriate model for these data. **(1 mark)**

Using the Poisson model with mean 2.59, expected frequencies corresponding to the given frequencies were calculated, to 2 decimal places, and are shown in the table below.

Number of plants	0	1	2	3	4	5	6	7 or greater
Expected frequencies	11.10	28.76	s	32.15	20.82	10.78	4.65	t

c Find the values of s and t to 2 decimal places. **(2 marks)**

d Stating clearly your hypotheses, test at the 5% level of significance whether or not this Poisson model is supported by these data. **(5 marks)**

6.5 Testing the goodness of fit with continuous data

When dealing with continuous data, you have to group the values into classes and then find the frequency for each class.

Testing a continuous uniform distribution as a model

The conditions under which a **continuous uniform distribution** is likely to arise are:

- symmetry about the mean

- classes of equal width have equal probabilities

A random variable X having a continuous uniform distribution over the interval (a, β) has a probability distribution function

$$f(x) = \begin{cases} \dfrac{1}{\beta - \alpha} & \alpha < x < \beta \\ 0 & \text{otherwise} \end{cases}$$

This distribution is continuous and so the observations must be put into classes which do not overlap (i.e. which are mutually exclusive). You will be calculating probabilities such as $P(a < x < b)$ using

$$P(a < X < b) = \frac{b - a}{\beta - \alpha}$$

There is only one constraint for the continuous uniform distribution – that the observed frequencies and the expected frequencies are the same. Therefore the degrees of freedom are

v = number of cells (after combining) −1

Example (13)   **SKILLS**   DECISION MAKING; REASONING/ARGUMENTATION

In a study on the habits of a group of birds, the direction which they left their home in the morning was recorded over 240 days. The direction was found by recording their bearing.

Bearing	$0 \leqslant d < 58$	$58 \leqslant d < 100$	$100 \leqslant d < 127$	$127 \leqslant d < 190$	$190 \leqslant d < 256$	$256 \leqslant d < 296$	$296 \leqslant d < 360$
Frequency	31	40	47	40	32	30	20

It is suggested that they leave their homes equally in all directions.

a Suggest a suitable **model**.

b Test at the 5% significance level to see if these data support this view.

---

a A suitable model would be $U \sim (0, 360)$

b H_0: The continuous uniform distribution is a suitable model.

H_1: The continuous uniform distribution is not a suitable model.

Class a to b	$b - a$	$P(a < X < b)$ $\dfrac{b - a}{360 - 0}$	Frequency $P(a < X < b) \times n$ $P(a < X < b) \times 240$
$0 \leqslant d < 58$	58	0.1661	38.67
$58 \leqslant d < 100$	42	0.1167	28
$100 \leqslant d < 127$	27	0.075	18
$127 \leqslant d < 190$	63	0.175	42
$190 \leqslant d < 256$	66	0.1833	44
$256 \leqslant d < 296$	40	0.1111	26.66
$296 \leqslant d < 360$	64	0.1778	42.67

> Calculate the frequencies, checking that they add up to 240

There are $7 - 1 = 6$ degrees of freedom and so we look at the χ_6^2 distribution.

> No parameter has been estimated so the only constraint is the usual one.

Class	O_i	E_i	$\dfrac{(O_i - E_i)^2}{E_i}$	$\dfrac{O_i^2}{E_i}$
$0 \leqslant d < 58$	31	38.67	1.5213	24.851
$58 \leqslant d < 100$	40	28	5.1429	57.143
$100 \leqslant d < 127$	47	18	46.7222	122.722
$127 \leqslant d < 190$	40	42	0.0952	38.095
$190 \leqslant d < 256$	32	44	3.2727	23.273
$256 \leqslant d < 296$	30	26.66	0.4184	33.758
$296 \leqslant d < 360$	20	42.67	12.0443	9.374

> Calculate the test statistic.
>
> Due to rounding, there may be a very small difference between and $\sum \dfrac{(O_i - E_i)^2}{E_i}$ and $\sum \dfrac{O_i^2}{E_i} - N$

$$X^2 = \sum \frac{(O_i - E_i)^2}{E_i} = 69.22 \text{ (2 d.p.)}$$

or

$$X^2 = \sum \frac{O_i^2}{E_i} - N = 309.22 - 240 = 69.22 \text{ (2 d.p.)}$$

From the table $\chi_6^2(0.05) = 12.592$ ⸱—————————— Find the critical value.

$X^2 > 12.592$ ⸱————————————————————— See if it is significant.

Therefore we reject H_0
The continuous uniform distribution is not a suitable model.
The birds do not leave home equally in all directions. ⸱——— Draw your conclusion.

Testing a normal distribution as a model

The conditions under which a normal distribution is likely to arise are:

- symmetry about the mean
- the distribution is 'bell-shaped'
- approximately two-thirds of the data falls within one standard deviation of the mean

The normal distribution has two parameters: μ the population mean and σ^2 the population variance. The degrees of freedom chosen in a hypothesis test will depend on whether we are estimating one, two or none of these parameters.

The estimate for μ is

$$\bar{x} = \frac{\Sigma x_i}{n}$$

and for σ^2 is

$$s^2 = \frac{\Sigma(x_i - \bar{x})^2}{n - 1} = \frac{1}{n - 1}\left(\Sigma x_i^2 - \frac{(\Sigma x_i)^2}{n}\right)$$

This distribution is continuous and so the observations must be put into classes which do not overlap. You will be calculating probabilities such as $P(a \leqslant x < b)$ using:

$$P(a \leqslant X < b) = P\left(\frac{a - \mu}{\sigma} \leqslant Z < \frac{b - \mu}{\sigma}\right)$$

$$= \Phi\left(\frac{b - \mu}{\sigma}\right) - \Phi\left(\frac{a - \mu}{\sigma}\right)$$

Links You learned how to find probabilities from the normal distribution in Statistics 1.
← **Statistics 1 Section 7.2**

The degrees of freedom chosen in a hypothesis test will depend on whether we are estimating none, one or two of these parameters:

If estimating none of the parameters,

v = number of cells (after combining) − 1

If estimating one of the parameters,

v = number of cells (after combining) − 2

If estimating two of the parameters,

v = number of cells (after combining) − 3

Example 14

During observations on the height of 200 male students the following data were observed.

Height (cm)	150-154	155-159	160-164	165-169	170-174	175-179	180-184	185-189	190-194
Frequency	4	6	12	30	64	52	18	10	4

a Test at the 5% significance level to see if the height of male students could be modelled by a normal distribution with mean 172 and standard deviation of 6.

b Describe how you would change this test if you were asked whether or not the height of male students could be modelled by a normal distribution with unknown mean and standard deviation.

a H_0: $X \sim N(172, 6^2)$ is a suitable model

H_1: $X \sim N(172, 6^2)$ is not a suitable model

State your hypotheses.

Links The classes need to use the true class boundaries.

← Statistics 1 Chapter 2

Class	$\dfrac{b - \mu}{\sigma}$	$P(a \leq X < b)$ $\Phi\left(\dfrac{b-\mu}{\sigma}\right) - \Phi\left(\dfrac{a-\mu}{\sigma}\right)$	$P(a \leq X < b) \times n$ $P(a \leq X < b) \times 200$
$X < 154.5$	-2.92	$0.0019 - 0 = 0.0019$	0.38
$154.5 \leq X < 159.5$	-2.08	$0.0188 - 0.0019$ $= 0.0169$	3.38
$159.5 \leq X < 164.5$	-1.25	$0.1056 - 0.0188$ $= 0.0868$	17.36
$164.5 \leq X < 169.5$	-0.42	$0.3372 - 0.1056$ $= 0.2316$	46.32
$169.5 \leq X < 174.5$	0.42	$0.6628 - 0.3372$ $= 0.3256$	65.12
$174.5 \leq X < 179.5$	1.25	$0.8944 - 0.6628$ $= 0.2316$	46.32
$179.5 \leq X < 184.5$	2.08	$0.9812 - 0.8944$ $= 0.0869$	17.36
$184.5 \leq X < 189.5$	2.92	$0.9981 - 0.9812$ $= 0.0169$	3.38
$X \geq 189.5$		$1 - 0.9981 = 0.0019$	0.38

The probabilities have been calculated by using the normal distribution tables.

Class	O_i	E_i	$\dfrac{(O_i - E_i)^2}{E_i}$	$\dfrac{O_i^2}{E_i}$
150-164	22	21.12	0.0367	22.917
165-169	30	46.32	5.7501	19.430
170-174	64	65.12	0.0193	62.899
175-179	52	46.32	0.6965	58.377
180-194	32	21.12	5.6048	48.485

Combine cells where $E_i < 5$

$$X^2 = \sum \frac{(O_i - E_i)^2}{E_i} = 12.11 \ (2 \ d.p.)$$

or

$$X^2 = \sum \frac{O_i^2}{E_i} - N = 212.11 - 200 = 12.11 \ (2 \ d.p.)$$

Since we are not estimating any parameters, •————— Find the critical value.

the number of degrees of freedom is $v = 5 - 1 = 4$

From the tables, $\chi_4^2(0.05) = 9.488$

$X^2 > 9.488$ •————————————————— See if it is significant.

We reject H_0

Therefore the normal distribution $N(172, 6^2)$ is not a suitable model. •————— Draw your conclusion.

b We would now need to estimate the parameters:

	midpoints	frequency	fx	fx^2
150-154	152	4	608	92 416
155-159	157	6	942	147 894
160-164	162	12	1944	314 298
165-169	167	30	5010	836 670
170-174	172	64	11 008	1 893 376
175-179	177	52	9204	1 629 108
180-184	182	18	3276	596 232
185-189	187	10	1870	349 690
190-194	192	4	768	147 456

We use the midpoints of the classes.

$\Sigma fx = 34\,630$

$\Sigma fx^2 = 6\,007\,770$

$n = 200$

$$\bar{x} = \frac{\Sigma fx}{n} = \frac{34\,630}{200} = 173.15$$

$$s^2 = \frac{1}{n-1}\left(\Sigma fx^2 - \frac{(\Sigma fx)^2}{n}\right) = \frac{1}{199}\left(6\,007\,770 - \frac{34\,630^2}{200}\right) = 58.22$$

H_0: a normal distribution is a good model •————— Restate the hypotheses.

H_1: a normal distribution is not a good model

We would now have $v = 5 - 1 - 2 = 2$ degrees of freedom.

Exercise **6E**   **SKILLS** CRITICAL THINKING; REASONING/ARGUMENTATION

1 The diameters of a random sample of 30 mass-produced discs were measured by passing them through various sized holes. Of the 30 discs, 18 passed through a 4.0 mm hole and of these, 6 did not pass through a 3.5 mm hole. Test the hypothesis that the diameters of the discs were a sample of a normal population with mean 3.8 mm and standard deviation 0.5 mm. Use a 5% significance level for your test.

2 An egg producer takes a sample of 150 eggs from his chickens and grades them into classes according to their weights in this table.

Class	2	3	4	5	6
Weight	66–70	61–65	56–60	51–55	46–50
Frequency	10	32	67	29	12

Does this distribution fit a normal distribution of mean 58 g and standard deviation 4 g? Use a 5% significance level for your test.

3 A sample of 100 apples is taken from an orchard. The apples have the following distribution of sizes:

Diameter (cm)	≤ 6	7	8	9	≥ 10
Frequency	8	29	38	16	9

It is thought that they come from a normal distribution with mean diameter of 8 cm and a standard deviation of 0.9 cm. Test this belief using a 5% level of significance.

4 A shop owner found that the number of cans of a drink sold per day during 100 days in summer was as shown in the table.

Drinks per day, d	0 –	10 –	20 –	30 –	40–50
Frequency of d	10	24	45	14	7

It is thought that these data can be modelled by a normal distribution.

a Estimate values of μ and σ and carry out a goodness of fit test using a 1% significance level.

b Explain how the shop owner might use this model.

5 A tailor sells boys' coats available in four sizes.

Size	Height
1	Up to 1.25 m
2	1.26–1.31 m
3	1.32–1.37 m
4	over 1.38 m

To help the tailor decide the stock levels he should order each year, the heights of 120 boys in the right age range were measured with the following results:

Height, h (m)	1.20–1.22	1.23–1.25	1.26–1.28	1.29–1.31
Frequency of h	9	9	18	23

Height, h (m)	1.32–1.34	1.35–1.37	1.38–1.40	1.41–1.43
Frequency of h	20	19	17	5

It is suggested that a suitable model for these data would be N(1.32, 0.042)

a Carry out a goodness of fit test using a 2.5% significance level.

b Estimate values of μ and σ using the observed values, and using these, carry out a goodness of fit using a 2.5% significance level.

c Select the best model and use it to advise the tailor how many of each size coat should be ordered each year if the usual annual sales are 1200.

6 The number of flowers as measured from a central point in a garden is thought to be modelled as a continuous uniform distribution. The distance from the centre of the garden is recorded for each flower. The results are summarised in the table below.

Distance from the centre of the garden (*m*)	0–1	1–2	2–4	4–6	6–9	9–12
Number of flowers	37	38	56	47	58	64

Test, at the 5% level of significance, whether or not the data can be modelled by a continuous uniform distribution. State your hypotheses clearly.

6.6 Using contingency tables

So far in this chapter you have considered the frequency with which a single event occurs. For example, you might count the number of times each of the numbers 1 to 6 appears when a dice is rolled 100 times. Sometimes however, we may be interested in the frequencies with which two **criteria** are met at the same time. If you study the frequency of A, B and C History grades, you may also want to know which of two schools the students attended. Here you have two criteria: the pass level and the school. You can show these results by means of a **contingency table** which shows the frequency with which each of the results occurred at each school separately.

		Pass (criterion 1)				
		A	**B**	**C**	**Totals**	
School (criterion 2)	*X*	18	12	20	50	— 18 students at school *X* got a grade A pass.
	Y	26	12	32	70	— 32 students at school *Y* got a grade C pass.
Totals		44	24	52	120	— 44 students out of a total of 120 got a grade A pass.

This is called a **2 × 3** contingency table since there are two rows and three columns.

Setting the hypotheses

We want to know if there is any association between the two schools' sets of results.

H_0: There is no association between the school and pass grade (school and pass grade are independent).

H_1: There is an association between school and pass grade (school and pass grade are not independent).

Selecting a model

If the hypothesis H_0 is true, then you would expect school X to get $\frac{50}{120}$ of each grade and school Y to get $\frac{70}{120}$ of each grade.

Now, overall: $P(\text{A grade}) = \frac{44}{120}$

$P(\text{school } X) = \frac{50}{120}$

So

$P(\text{A grade and school } X) = P(\text{A grade}) \times P(\text{school } X) = \frac{44}{120} \times \frac{50}{120}$

The expected frequency of an A grade from school X is therefore:

$$\frac{44}{120} \times \frac{50}{120} \times 120 = \frac{44 \times 50}{120} = 18.33$$

Notice that:

- **Expected frequency** $= \dfrac{\text{row total} \times \text{column total}}{\text{grand total}}$

The expected frequency is calculated on the assumption that the criteria are independent. You can find the other expected frequencies in the same way. These are shown in the table.

		Pass (criterion 1)			
		A	**B**	**C**	**Totals**
School (criterion 2)	X	$\frac{50 \times 44}{120} = 18.33$	$\frac{50 \times 24}{120} = 10$	$\frac{50 \times 52}{120} = 21.67$	50
	Y	$\frac{70 \times 44}{120} = 25.67$	$\frac{70 \times 24}{120} = 14$	$\frac{70 \times 52}{120} = 30.33$	70
Totals		44	24	52	120

Degrees of freedom

When calculating expected values, you need not calculate the last value in each row. This is because the sum of the values in each row has to equal the row total.

> This creates one constraint on the number of degrees of freedom.

For example, the expected frequency of students who obtain a grade C from school X would be $50 - (18.33 + 10) = 21.67$

In the same way, the last value in each column is fixed by the column total once the other values in the column are known.

> This creates another constraint on the number of degrees of freedom.

For example, the expected frequency of students who obtain a grade A from school Y would be $44 - 18.33 = 25.67$

In general, if there are h rows, then once $(h - 1)$ expected frequencies have been calculated the last value in the row is fixed by the row total. If there are k columns, once $(k - 1)$ columns have been calculated the last column value is fixed by the column total.

The number of independent variables is given therefore by $(h - 1)(k - 1)$. That is to say:

- **The number of degrees of freedom**
  $\nu = (h - 1)(k - 1)$

> **Watch out** If the expected frequency in any column is < 5, you will need to combine columns. Make sure you use the new number of columns after combining as your value of k when working out the number of degrees of freedom.

Example 15

Carry out a goodness of fit test, at the 5% significance level, for the data given at the start of this section for the two schools X and Y.

H_0: There is no association between school and pass grade.

Form your hypotheses.

H_1: There is an association between school and pass grade.

$\nu = (h - 1)(k - 1) = (2 - 1)(3 - 1) = 2$

Calculate the number of degrees of freedom.

From tables, the critical value at the 5% significance level is 5.991

Find the critical value.

O_i	E_i	$\dfrac{(O_i - E_i)^2}{E_i}$
18	18.33	0.0059
12	10.00	0.4000
20	21.67	0.1287
26	25.67	0.0042
12	14.00	0.2857
32	30.33	0.0920

The expected values have already been calculated in the table on page 117.

$$\sum \frac{(O_i - E_i)^2}{E_i} = 0.9165$$

Calculate $\sum \dfrac{(O_i - E_i)^2}{E_i}$ or $\sum \dfrac{O_i^2}{E_i} - N$

So: $\sum \dfrac{(O_i - E_i)^2}{E_i} < 5.991$

See if the value is significant.

Do not reject H_0: there is insufficient evidence to suggest an association between the school and the pass grades.

School and pass grade are independent.

Draw a conclusion.

Example 16

During the trial of a new medicine, 60 volunteers out of 200 were treated with the medicine. Those who experienced relief of their symptoms and those who did not were recorded as in the table.

	Relief	No relief	Totals
Treated	10	50	60
Not treated	40	100	140
Totals	50	150	200

Use a suitable test to see if there is any association between treatment with the medicine and symptoms getting better. Use a 5% significance level.

H_0: There is no association between treatment and relief.

Form your hypotheses.

H_1: There is an association between treatment and relief.

Table of expected values:

	Relief	No relief
Treated	$\dfrac{60 \times 50}{200} = 15$	$\dfrac{60 \times 150}{200} = 45$
Not treated	$\dfrac{140 \times 50}{200} = 35$	$\dfrac{140 \times 150}{200} = 105$

Calculate the expected values.

$\nu = (2-1)(2-1) = 1$

Find the degrees of freedom.

From the table on page 142, the critical value $\chi_1^2(5\%)$ is 3.841

O_i	E_i	$\dfrac{(O_i - E_i)^2}{E_i}$
10	15	1.6667
50	45	0.5556
40	35	0.7143
100	105	0.2381

$$\sum \frac{(O_i - E_i)^2}{E_i} = 3.1747$$

Calculate $\sum \dfrac{(O_i - E_i)^2}{E_i}$ or $\sum \dfrac{O_i^2}{E_i} - N$

$$\sum \frac{(O_i - E_i)^2}{E_i} < 3.841$$

See if your value is significant.

So you do not reject H_0. There is no reason to believe there is an association between treatment and relief.

Draw a conclusion.

Exercise 6F **SKILLS** REASONING/ARGUMENTATION

1 When analysing the results of a 3 × 2 contingency table it was found that:

$$\sum_{i=1}^{6} \frac{(O_i - E_i)^2}{E_i} = 2.38$$

Write down the number of degrees of freedom and the critical value appropriate to these data in order to carry out a χ^2 test of significance at the 5% level.

2 Three different types of city were studied to see whether owning a television was related to the type of city or not. $\sum \dfrac{(O_i - E_i)^2}{E_i}$ was calculated and found to be 13.1.

Using a 5% level of significance, carry out a suitable test and state your conclusion.

3 In a college, three different groups of students sit the same examination. The results of the examination are classified as Credit, Pass or Fail. In order to test whether or not there is an association between the group and exam results, the statistic $\sum \dfrac{(O_i - E_i)^2}{E_i}$ is calculated and found to be equal to 10.28.

a Explain why there are 4 degrees of freedom in this situation.

b Using a 5% level of significance, carry out the test and state your conclusions.

(E) **4** The grades of 200 students in both Mathematics and English were studied with the following results.

Using a 5% significance level, test these results to see if there is an association between English and Mathematics results. State your conclusions. **(6 marks)**

		English grades		
		A	**B**	**C**
Mathematics grades	**A**	17	28	18
	B	38	45	16
	C	12	12	14

(E) **5** The number of trains on time and the number of trains that were late were observed at three different Beijing stations, with the results shown here.

Using the χ^2 statistic and a significance test at the 5% level, decide if there is any association between station and lateness. **(6 marks)**

		Observed frequency	
		On time	**Late**
Station	*A*	26	14
	B	30	10
	C	44	26

6 200 students are classified into grades A, B, C, D and E. They are also classified as male or female, and their results are summarised in a contingency table.

Assuming all expected values are 5 or more, the statistic $\sum \frac{(O_i - E_i)^2}{E_i}$ was 14.27.

Stating your hypotheses and using a 1% significance level, investigate whether or not gender and grade are associated.

7 In a random sample of 60 articles made in factory *A*, 13 were **defective**. In factory *B*, 12 out of 40 similar articles were defective.

a Draw up a contingency table.

b Test at the 5% significance level the hypothesis that quality was independent of the factory involved.

8 During a flu epidemic, 15 boys and 8 girls became ill out of a year group of 22 boys and 28 girls. Assuming that this group may be treated as a random sample of the age group, test at the 5% significance level the hypothesis that there is no connection between gender and how easy it is to catch flu.

(E) **9** In a study of sea animals, a biologist collected specimens from three beaches and counted the number of males and females in each sample, with the following results:

Using a significance level of 5%, test these results to see if there is any association between the choice of beach and the gender of the animals. **(6 marks)**

		Beach		
		A	*B*	*C*
Gender	**Male**	46	80	40
	Female	54	120	160

(E) **10** A research worker studying the ages of adults and the number of bank cards they own obtained the results shown in this table.

Use the χ^2 statistic and a significance test at the 5% level to decide whether or not there is an association between age and number of bank cards owned.

		Number of cards	
		$\leqslant 3$	> 3
Age	$\leqslant 30$	74	20
	> 30	50	35

(6 marks)

(E) **11** Members of four local gyms were surveyed to find out if they had injured themselves while working out in the last month. The results are summarised in the table below:

	Gym				
	A	*B*	*C*	*D*	Totals
Injured	15	4	8	7	34
Uninjured	222	254	167	188	831
Totals	237	258	175	195	865

A test is carried out at the 5% significance level to determine whether or not there is an association between injuries and choice of gym.

a State the null hypothesis for this test. **(1 mark)**

b Show that the expected frequency of members injured at gym *C* is 6.88 **(1 mark)**

c Calculate the test statistic for this test, and state with reasons whether or not the null hypothesis is rejected. **(5 marks)**

(E/P) **12** Millie wants to investigate whether students who studied different sciences at university get paid the same when they get a job. She surveys science graduates who graduated from university in the last 5 years, and records their salary information. The results are recorded in the table below.

		Salary					
		£0–£20k	£20k–£40k	£40k–£60k	£60k–£80k	>£80k	Totals
Science studied	**Biology**	4	69	23	5	3	104
	Chemistry	3	72	27	4	2	108
	Physics	2	68	32	5	4	111
	Totals	9	209	82	14	9	323

She tests at the 5% significance level whether there is an association between the science studied and salary.

a State the null and alternative hypotheses for this test. **(1 mark)**

b Calculate the test statistic for this test, and state with reasons whether or not the null hypothesis is rejected. **(5 marks)**

Problem-solving

If any of the expected frequencies are less than 5 you have to combine columns before calculating X^2.

Chapter review 6

1 The random variable Y has a χ^2 distribution with 10 degrees of freedom.
Find y such that $P(Y < y) = 0.99$

2 The random variable X has a χ^2 distribution with 8 degrees of freedom.
Find x such that $P(X > x) = 0.05$

3 As part of an investigation into visits to a health centre, a 5×3 contingency table was constructed. A χ^2 test of significance at the 5% level is to be carried out on the table.
Write down the number of degrees of freedom and the critical region appropriate to this test.

4 Data are collected in the form of a 4×4 contingency table.
To carry out a χ^2 test of significance, one of the rows is combined with another row and the resulting value of $\sum \dfrac{(O - E)^2}{E}$ was calculated.

Write down the number of degrees of freedom and the critical value of χ^2 appropriate to this test, assuming a 5% significance level.

(E) 5 A new medicine to treat the common cold was used with a randomly selected group of 100 volunteers. Each was given the medicine and their health was monitored to see if they caught a cold. A randomly selected control group

	Cold	No cold
Medicine	34	66
Placebo	45	55

of 100 volunteers was treated with a placebo (a substance used as a control in testing new drugs). The results are shown in the table above.

Using a 5% significance level, test whether or not the chance of catching a cold is affected by taking the new medicine. State your hypotheses carefully. **(6 marks)**

(E/P) 6 Breakdowns on a certain stretch of highway were recorded each day for 80 consecutive days. The results are summarised in the table here.

Number of breakdowns	0	1	2	> 2
Frequency	38	32	10	0

It is suggested that the number of breakdowns per day can be modelled by a Poisson distribution.

Using a 5% significance level, test whether or not the Poisson distribution is a suitable model for these data. State your hypotheses clearly. **(9 marks)**

(E) 7 A survey in a college was created to investigate whether or not there was any association between gender and passing a driving test. 50 males and 50 females were asked whether they passed or failed their driving test at the first attempt. All the students asked had taken the test. The results are given in the table.

	Pass	Fail
Male	23	27
Female	32	18

Stating your hypotheses clearly, test, at the 10% level, whether or not there is any evidence of an association between gender and passing a driving test at the first attempt. **(6 marks)**

8 Successful contestants (people who take part in a contest) in a TV game show were allowed to select from one of five boxes, numbered 1 to 5. Four of the boxes contained prizes and one of them contained nothing.

Box number	1	2	3	4	5
Frequency	20	16	25	18	21

After the show had run for 100 weeks, the choices made by the contestants were analysed with the results given in the table above.

  a Explain why these data could possibly be modelled by a discrete uniform distribution.

  b Using a significance level of 5%, test to see if the discrete uniform distribution is a good model in this particular case.

(E/P) **9** A bug spray was tested on 50 samples of five flies. The numbers of dead flies after 1 hour were then counted with the results given in this table.

Number of dead flies	0	1	2	3	4	5
Frequency	1	1	5	11	24	8

  a Calculate the probability that a fly dies when sprayed. **(2 marks)**

  b Using a significance level of 5%, test to see if these data could be modelled by a binomial distribution. **(5 marks)**

(E/P) **10** The number of accidents per week on a certain road was monitored for four years. The results obtained are summarised in the table.

Number of accidents	0	1	2	>2
Frequency	112	56	40	0

Using a 5% level of significance, carry out a χ^2 test of the hypothesis that the number of accidents per week has a Poisson distribution. **(9 marks)**

(E/P) **11** Samples of rocks were taken at two sites on a beach which were one mile apart. The rocks were classified as igneous, sedimentary or other types, with the following results.

		Site	
		A	*B*
Rock type	Igneous	30	10
	Sedimentary	55	35
	Other	15	15

A scientist believes that the distribution of rock types at site *A* can be used as a model for the distribution at site *B*. Test this belief, using a 5% significance level. **(6 marks)**

(E/P) **12** A small shop sells a particular item at a fairly steady yearly rate. When looking at the weekly sales, it was found that the number sold varied. The results for the 50 weeks the shop was open were as shown in the table.

Weekly sales	0	1	2	3	4	5	6	7	8	>8
Frequency	0	4	7	8	10	6	7	4	4	0

  a Find the mean number of sales per week. **(2 marks)**

  b Using a significance level of 5%, test to see if these can be modelled by a Poisson distribution. **(8 marks)**

(E) 13 A study was done to see how many students in a college were left-handed and how many were right-handed. As well as left- or right-handedness, the gender of each person was also recorded with the results given in this table.

	Left-handed	Right-handed
Male	100	600
Female	80	800

Use a significance test at the 5% level to see if there is an association between gender and left- and right-handedness.　　**(6 marks)**

(E) 14 A school science department collected data on which science subject students found the most interesting. A random sample of 300 students gave these results.

		Subject		
		Physics	Biology	Chemistry
Gender	Male	74	28	68
	Female	45	40	45

A test is carried out at the 1% level of significance to determine whether or not there is an association between gender and preferred subject.

a State the null hypothesis for this test.　　**(1 mark)**

b Show that the expected frequency for females choosing Biology is 29.47 (to 2 d.p.)　　**(1 mark)**

c Calculate the remaining expected frequencies, and the test statistic for this test.　　**(3 marks)**

d State whether or not the null hypothesis should be rejected. Justify your answer.　　**(2 marks)**

e Would the test be rejected if instead the test was carried out at the 5% level of significance?　　**(1 mark)**

(E) 15 The discrete random variable X follows a Poisson distribution with mean 2.15

a Write down the values of:

  i $P(X = 1)$

  ii $P(X > 2)$　　**(2 marks)**

The manager at a call centre recorded the number of calls coming in each minute between noon and 1 p.m.

Number of calls	0	1	2	3	4	5	6	Total
Frequency	10	12	14	12	8	3	1	60

b Show that the average number of calls received in a minute is 2.15　　**(1 mark)**

The manager believes that the Poisson distribution may be a model for the number of calls arriving each minute. She uses a Poisson distribution with mean 2.15 to calculate expected frequencies as follows.

Number of calls	0	1	2	3	4	5	6 or more
Expected frequency	6.99	15.03	a	11.58	6.22	2.67	b

c Find the values of a and b to 2 decimal places.　　**(2 marks)**

The manager will test, at the 5% level of significance, if the data can be modelled by a Poisson distribution as she suspects.

d State the null and alternative hypotheses for this test.　　**(1 mark)**

    e   Explain why the last two cells in the expected frequency table
        should be combined when calculating the test statistic for this test.   **(1 mark)**

    f   Calculate the test statistic and state the conclusion for this test.
       State clearly the critical value used in the test.   **(4 marks)**

16   A tensile test is carried out on 100 steel bars which are uniform in section. The distances from the mid-points of the bars at which they fracture is recorded with the following results.

Distance	$0 \leqslant d < 10$	$10 \leqslant d < 20$	$20 \leqslant d < 30$	$30 \leqslant d < 40$	$40 \leqslant d < 50$	$50 \leqslant d < 60$
Frequency	15	17	18	20	12	18

Test at the 5% significance level whether or not these data can be modelled by a continuous uniform distribution.

(E) **17**   A random sample of 500 phone calls to a call centre revealed the following distribution of call length (in minutes).

Length of call	$0 \leqslant l < 5$	$5 \leqslant l < 10$	$10 \leqslant l < 15$	$15 \leqslant l < 20$	$20 \leqslant l < 25$
Frequency	7	63	221	177	32

    a   Estimate the mean and variance of the call lengths.

    b   Using the mean and variance calculated in part **a**, test at the 5% level of significance whether call length can be modelled by a normal distribution.

Summary of key points

1   The **null** and **alternative hypotheses** generally take the following form:

   H_0: There is no difference between the observed and the theoretical distribution.

   H_1: There is a difference between the observed and the theoretical distribution.

2   **Goodness of fit** is concerned with measuring how well an observed frequency distribution fits to a known distribution.

3   The measure of goodness of fit is $X^2 = \sum \dfrac{(O_i - E_i)^2}{E_i}$ or $X^2 = \sum \dfrac{O_i^2}{E_i} - N$

4   The χ^2 family of distributions can be used to approximate X^2 as long as none of the expected values is below 5.

5   When calculating **degrees of freedom**:

      ν = number of cells after combining − number of constraints

6   When using chi-squared tests, if any of the expected values are less than 5, then you combine frequencies in the data table until they are greater than 5.

7 When selecting which member of the χ^2 family to use as an approximation for X^2, you must select the distribution which has ν equal to the number of degrees of freedom of your expected values.

8 If X^2 exceeds the critical value, it is unlikely that the null hypothesis is correct, so you reject it in favour of the alternative hypothesis.

9 If n is the number of cells after combining:

Distribution	Degrees of freedom	
	Parameters known	**Parameters not known**
Discrete uniform	$n-1$	
Binomial	$n-1$	$n-2$
Poisson	$n-1$	$n-2$

Continuous uniform $n-1$

Normal $n-1$, then $n-2$ if one parameter not known, and $n-3$ if both parameters not known

10 For contingency tables:

$$\textbf{expected frequency} = \frac{\text{row total} \times \text{column total}}{\text{grand total}}$$

for an $h \times k$ table, the number of degrees of freedom $\nu = (h-1)(k-1)$

Review exercise

2

E/P **1** A report on the population stated that the mean height of three-year-old children is 90 cm and the standard deviation is 5 cm. A sample of 100 three-year-old children was chosen from the population.

  a Write down the distribution of the sample mean height. **(2)**

  b Hence, find the probability that the sample mean height is at least 91 cm. **(3)**

  ← **Statistics 3 Section 4.1**

E/P **2** A sample of size 5 is taken from a population that is normally distributed with mean 10 and standard deviation 3.

  Find the probability that the sample mean lies between 7 and 10. **(4)**

  ← **Statistics 3 Section 4.1**

E/P **3** The random variable X has the probability distribution shown in the table:

x	1	2	3	4
$P(X = x)$	0.4	$2k$	0.3	k

  a Find the value of k. **(2)**

  A random sample of 200 observations of X is taken.

  b Use the central limit theorem to estimate the probability that the mean of these observations is greater than 2.09 **(6)**

  c Comment on the accuracy of your estimate. **(1)**

  ← **Statistics 3 Section 4.1**

E/P **4** A busy call centre receives, on average, 15 calls every minute.

  a Calculate the probability that fewer than 10 calls come in a given minute. **(1)**

  b Find the probability that in one 30-minute period no more than 420 calls come in. **(2)**

  c Use the central limit theorem to estimate the probability that in one 30-minute period no more than 420 calls come in. Compare your answer to part **b**. **(5)**

  ← **Statistics 3 Section 4.2**

E/P **5** A bag contains a large number of coloured balls, red and green, in the ratio 3 : 1. Twenty students each repeatedly select a ball from the bag and then replace it, continuing until a green ball is selected.

  Use the central limit theorem to estimate the probability that the mean number of attempts needed to select a green ball is more than 4.5 **(5)**

  ← **Statistics 3 Section 4.2**

E/P **6** A group of students are completing a multiple-choice quiz where there are five answers to each question.

  One student is chosen at random. Given that the student guesses each answer,

  a find the probability that the student gets the 4th question correct on the 12th attempt. **(2)**

  b Find the expected number of questions the student must answer to get four correct answers. **(2)**

  There are 15 students in the group. Each student continues answering questions until they have achieved four correct answers.

  c Estimate the probability that the mean number of questions answered per student is less than 19. **(5)**

  ← **Statistics 3 Section 4.2**

7 During a village show, two judges, *P* and *Q*, had to award a mark out of 30 to some flower displays. The marks they awarded to a random sample of 8 displays are shown in the table below.

Display	A	B	C	D	E	F	G	H
Judge *P*	25	19	21	23	28	17	16	20
Judge *Q*	20	9	21	13	17	14	11	15

a Calculate Spearman's rank correlation coefficient for the marks awarded by the two judges. **(4)**

After the show, one person complained about the judges. She claimed that there was no positive correlation between their marks.

b Stating your hypotheses clearly, test whether this sample provides support for the person's claim. Use a 5% level of significance. **(4)**

← Statistics 3 Sections 5.2, 5.3

8 The table below shows the price of the same ice cream at different stands on a beach, and the distance of each stand from the pier.

Stand	Distance from pier (m)	Price (£)
A	50	1.75
B	175	1.20
C	270	2.00
D	375	1.05
E	425	0.95
F	580	1.25
G	710	0.80
H	790	0.75
I	890	1.00
J	980	0.85

a Find, to 3 decimal places, the Spearman rank correlation coefficient between the distance of the stand from the pier and the price of the ice cream. **(4)**

b Stating your hypotheses clearly and using a 5% significance level, test for negative rank correlation between price and distance. **(4)**

← Statistics 3 Sections 5.2, 5.3

9 The numbers of deaths in one year from pneumoconiosis and lung cancer in a developing country are given below:

Age group (years)	Deaths from pneumoconiosis (1000s)	Deaths from lung cancer (1000s)
20–29	12.5	3.7
30–39	5.9	9
40–49	18.5	10.2
50–59	19.4	19
60–69	31.2	13
70 and over	31	18

A charity claims that the relative vulnerabilities of different age groups are similar for both diseases.

a Give one reason to support the use of Spearman's rank correlation coefficient in this instance. **(1)**

b Calculate Spearman's rank correlation coefficient for these data. **(4)**

c Test the charity's claim at the 5% significance level. State your hypotheses clearly. **(4)**

← Statistics 3 Sections 5.2, 5.3

10 The product moment correlation coefficient is denoted by *r* and Spearman's rank correlation coefficient is denoted by r_s.

a Sketch separate scatter diagrams, with five points on each diagram, to show:
i $r = 1$
ii $r_s = -1$ but $r > -1$

Two judges rank seven collie dogs in a competition. The collie dogs are labelled *A* to *G* and the rankings are as follows.

Rank	1	2	3	4	5	6	7
Judge 1	A	C	D	B	E	F	G
Judge 2	A	B	D	C	E	G	F

b i Calculate Spearman's rank correlation coefficient for these data.

ii Stating your hypotheses clearly, test, at the 5% level of significance, whether or not the judges are generally in agreement. **(8)**

← Statistics 3 Sections 5.1, 5.2, 5.3

(E) **11** The masses of a reactant t mg and a product p mg in ten different instances of a chemistry experiment were recorded in a table.

t	p
1.2	3.8
1.9	7
3.2	11
3.9	12
2.5	9
4.5	12
5.7	13.5
4	12.2
1.1	2
5.9	13.9

You may use $\sum t^2 = 141.51$, $\sum p^2 = 1081.74$ and $\sum tp = 386.32$

a Draw a scatter diagram to represent these data. **(2)**

b State what is measured by the product moment correlation coefficient. **(1)**

c Calculate S_{tt}, S_{pp} and S_{tp}. **(3)**

d Calculate the value of the product moment correlation coefficient r between t and p. **(2)**

e Stating your hypotheses clearly, test, at the 1% significance level, whether or not the correlation coefficient is greater than zero. **(4)**

f With reference to your scatter diagram, comment on your result in part **e**. **(1)**

← Statistics 3 Sections 5.1, 5.3

(E) **12** A geographer claims that the speed of the flow of water in a river gets slower as the river gets wider. He measures the width of the river, w metres, at seven points and records the rate of flow, f m s^{-1}.

Point	A	B	C	D	E	F	G
w	1.3	1.8	2.2	3.1	4.8	5.2	7.3
f	5.4	4.8	4.9	4.4	3.8	3.9	2.5

Spearman's rank correlation coefficient between w and f is -0.93

a Stating your hypotheses clearly, test whether or not the data provides support for the geographer's claim. Test at the 1% level of significance. **(4)**

b Without recalculating the correlation coefficient, explain how Spearman's rank correlation coefficient would change if:

i the speed of flow at G was actually 2.6 m s^{-1}

ii an extra measurement H was taken with a width of 0.8 m and a speed of flow of 6.2 m s^{-1}. **(3)**

The geographer collected data from a further 10 locations and found that there were now many tied ranks.

c Describe how you could find Spearman's rank correlation coefficient in this situation. **(2)**

← Statistics 3 Sections 5.1, 5.2

(E/P) **13** A factory manager regularly samples 20 items from a production line and records the number of defective items x. The results of 100 such samples are given below.

x	0	1	2	3	4	5	6	7 or more
Frequency	17	31	19	14	9	7	3	0

a Estimate the proportion of defective items from the production line. **(1)**

The manager claims that the number of defective items in a sample of 20 can be modelled by a binomial distribution. He uses the answer in part **a** to calculate the expected frequencies, given below.

x	0	1	2	3	4	5	6	7 or more
Expected frequency	12.2	27.0	r	19.0	s	3.2	0.9	0.2

b Find the value of r and the value of s, giving your answers to 1 decimal place.
(2)

c Stating your hypotheses clearly, use a 5% level of significance to test the manager's claim. **(6)**

d Explain what the analysis in part **c** tells the manager about the occurrence of defective items from this production line. **(2)**

← **Statistics 3 Sections 6.4**

(E/P) 14 Five coins were flipped 100 times and the number of heads recorded. The results are shown in the table below.

Number of heads	0	1	2	3	4	5
Frequency	6	18	29	34	10	3

a Suggest a suitable distribution to model the number of heads when five unbiased coins are flipped. **(1)**

b Test, at the 10% level of significance, whether or not the five coins are unbiased. State your hypotheses clearly. **(6)**

← **Statistics 3 Sections 6.4**

(E/P) 15 Ten cuttings were taken from each of 100 randomly selected garden plants. The number of cuttings that did not grow were recorded. The results are as follows.

Number which did not grow	0	1	2	3	4	5	6	7	8, 9 or 10
Frequency	11	21	30	20	12	3	2	1	0

a Show that the probability of a randomly selected cutting, from this sample, not growing is 0.223. **(2)**

A gardener believes that a binomial distribution might provide a good model for the number of cuttings, out of 10, that do not grow.

He uses a binomial distribution, with the probability 0.2 of a cutting not growing. The calculated expected frequencies are as follows.

Number which did not grow	0	1	2	3	4	5 or more
Expected frequency	r	26.84	s	20.13	8.81	t

b Find the values of r, s and t. **(3)**

c State clearly the hypotheses required to test whether or not this binomial distribution is a suitable model for these data. **(1)**

The test statistic for the test is 4.17 and the number of degrees of freedom used is 4.

d Explain fully why there are 4 degrees of freedom. **(2)**

e Stating clearly the critical value used, carry out the test using a 5% level of significance. **(4)**

← **Statistics 3 Section 6.4**

(E/P) 16 The number of times per day a computer fails and has to be restarted is recorded for 200 days. The results are summarised in the table.

Number of restarts	Frequency
0	99
1	65
2	22
3	12
4	2

Test whether or not a Poisson model is suitable to represent the number of restarts per day. Use a 5% level of significance and state your hypothesis clearly. **(6)**

← **Statistics 3 Sections 6.4**

(E/P) 17 The head teacher at a large school believes that students' grades in Mathematics are independent of their grades in English. She examined the results of a random group of candidates who had studied both subjects and she recorded the number of candidates in each of the 6 categories shown.

		Mathematics grade		
		A or B	C or D	E or U
English grade	A or B	25	25	10
	C to U	5	30	15

  a Stating your hypotheses clearly, test the head teacher's belief using a 10% level of significance. You must show each step of your working. **(7)**

An English teacher suggested that the head teacher was losing accuracy by combining the English grades C to U in one row. He suggested that the head teacher should split the English grades into two rows, grades C or D and grades E or U, as with Mathematics.

  b State why this might lead to problems in performing the test. **(2)**

← **Statistics 3 Sections 6.5**

(E) 18 People over the age of 65 are offered an annual flu injection. A health official took a random sample from a list of patients who were over 65. She recorded their gender and whether or not the offer of an annual flu injection was accepted or rejected. The results are summarised below.

	Accepted	Rejected
Male	170	110
Female	280	140

Using a 5% significance level, test whether or not there is an association between gender and acceptance or rejection of an annual flu injection. State your hypotheses clearly. **(7)**

← **Statistics 3 Sections 6.5**

(E) 19 Students in a college are classified as taking courses in either Arts, Science or Humanities. A random sample of students from the college gave the following results.

	Arts	Science	Humanities
Boy	30	50	35
Girl	40	20	42

Showing your working clearly, test, at the 1% level of significance, whether or not there is an association between gender and the type of course taken. State your hypotheses clearly. **(7)**

← **Statistics 3 Sections 6.5**

(E) 20 A researcher carried out a survey of three treatments for a fruit tree disease.

	No action	Remove diseased branches	Spray with chemicals
Tree died within 1 year	10	5	6
Tree survived for 1–4 years	5	9	7
Tree survived beyond 4 years	5	6	7

Test, at the 5% level of significance, whether or not there is any association between the treatment of the trees and their survival. State your hypotheses and conclusion clearly. **(7)**

← Statistics 3 Sections 6.5

(E) **21** A research worker studying colour preference and the age of a random sample of 50 children obtained the results shown below.

Age in years	Red	Blue	Totals
4	12	6	18
8	10	7	17
12	6	9	15
Totals	28	22	50

Using a 5% significance level, carry out a test to decide whether or not there is an association between age and colour preference. State your hypotheses clearly. **(7)**

← Statistics 3 Sections 6.5

(E) **22** An actor receives fan mail six days a week. She thinks that the deliveries of mail are uniformly distributed throughout the week. The deliveries over a five-week period are as follows:

Day	Mon	Tues	Wed	Thurs	Fri	Sat
Frequency	20	15	18	23	19	25

Test the actor's assertion using a 1% level of significance. **(6)**

← Statistics 3 Sections 6.4

Challenge

A manufacturer claims that the batteries used in his smartphones have a mean lifetime of 360 hours and a standard deviation of 20 hours, when the phone is left on standby. To test this claim, 100 phones were left on standby until the batteries ran flat. The lifetime t hours of the batteries was recorded. The results are as follows.

t	300–	320–	340–	350–	360–	370–	380–	400–
Frequency	1	9	28	20	16	18	7	1

A researcher believes that a normal distribution might provide a good model for the lifetime of the batteries. She calculated the expected frequencies as follows using the distribution N(360, 20).

t	< 320	320–	340–	350–	360–	370–	380–	400–
Expected frequency	2.28	13.59	24.26	r	s	14.98	13.59	2.28

a Find the values of r and s.

b Stating clearly your hypotheses, test, at the 1% level of significance, whether or not this normal distribution is a suitable model for these data.

← Statistics 3 Sections 6.4

Exam practice
Mathematics
International Advanced Subsidiary/ Advanced Level Statistics 3

Time: 1 hour 30 minutes
You must have: Mathematical Formulae and Statistical Tables, Calculator
Answer ALL questions

1 In a forest, there are 4 types of bird – Blackbird, Sparrow, Chaffinch and Woodpecker.
 They occur roughly in the ratio $4:2:2:1$. A scientist wants to see if there has been
 a change in the ratio of these birds, and she plans to take a sample of 360 birds.
 a Explain why quota sampling would be the most appropriate sampling technique. **(2)**
 b Describe how you would take a quota sample in this case. **(4)**

2 A group of ten students sat a computing examination split into two parts – theory and
 programming. Each student's scores are shown in the table below.

	A	B	C	D	E	F	G	H	I	J
theory	28	30	22	37	33	21	17	27	32	25
programming	51	50	38	53	57	44	40	42	46	27

 a Stating your hypotheses clearly, test, at the 5% level of significance, whether or not there
 is a positive correlation between the scores on the theory paper and the scores on the
 programming paper. **(10)**
 b Student I discovers his theory paper was marked incorrectly and should have been 33.
 Without further working, describe how you would adapt the hypothesis test. **(2)**

3 The waiting times for a train are observed over 150 days and the results are shown in the
 table below.

Time, t (min)	$0 \leqslant t < 10$	$10 \leqslant t < 20$	$20 \leqslant t < 30$	$30 \leqslant t < 40$	$40 \leqslant t < 50$	$50 \leqslant t < 60$
Frequency	21	30	20	14	33	32

 The departure time of the previous train is not known in each case. A passenger believes
 that the waiting times are uniformly distributed over one hour. Test this claim at the 10%
 level of significance. **(10)**

4 The independent random variables X and Y are defined as:

$X \sim N(10, 2^2)$ and $Y \sim N(15, 3^2)$

Let the random variable D be defined as $D = 5X - 3Y$.

Find:

a E(D) (2)

b Var(D) (3)

c P$(5X > 3Y)$ (3)

Three independent observations, X_1, X_2 and X_3 are taken from X.

The random variable $\overline{X} = \dfrac{X_1 + X_2 + X_3}{3}$

d Find P$(\overline{X} - X_3 < 1)$ (6)

5 Random samples of employees are taken from two chocolate manufacturing companies, A and B. Each employee is asked which type of chocolate (white, milk or dark) they prefer. The results are shown in the following table.

	White	Milk	Dark
A	50	44	21
B	25	28	32

Stating your hypotheses clearly, test to see if there is an association between an employee's chocolate preference and the company he or she works for, using a 5% level of significance. Show your working clearly.   (11)

6 A group of 40 children and 60 adults take part in a logic puzzle. The mean time taken for the children to complete the puzzle is 41.2 seconds, with a standard deviation of 3.6 seconds. For the adults, the mean time is 47.6 seconds with a standard deviation of 2.7 seconds.

Assuming the completion times are normally distributed with equal variances, test at the 2.5% significance level whether children complete the puzzle more than 5 seconds quicker than the adults.   (10)

7 The masses (m, in grams) of 50 snack bars are measured and the following summative statistics are given.

$\Sigma m = 13\,790 \quad \Sigma m^2 = 3\,803\,508$

a Find unbiased estimates for μ and σ^2 (4)

b Find a 95% confidence interval for the mean mass of a snack bar.   (4)

c State the importance of the central limit theorem in finding this confidence interval.   (2)

d Snack bars have the mass **275 g** printed on their wrappers. Without further calculation, does the confidence interval lead you to believe that this is correct? Give a reason for your answer.   (2)

TOTAL FOR PAPER: 75 MARKS

The Normal Distribution Function

The function tabulated below is $\Phi(z)$, defined as $\Phi(z) = \dfrac{1}{\sqrt{2\pi}} \displaystyle\int_{-\infty}^{z} e^{-\frac{1}{2}t^2}\, dt$

z	$\Phi(z)$	z	$\Phi(z)$	z	$\Phi(z)$	z	$\Phi(z)$	z	$\Phi(z)$
0.00	0.500	0.50	0.6915	1.00	0.8413	1.50	0.9332	2.00	0.9772
0.01	0.5040	0.51	0.6950	1.01	0.8438	1.51	0.9345	2.02	0.9783
0.02	0.5080	0.52	0.6985	1.02	0.8461	1.52	0.9357	2.04	0.9793
0.03	0.5120	0.53	0.7019	1.03	0.8485	1.53	0.9370	2.06	0.9803
0.04	0.5160	0.54	0.7054	1.04	0.8508	1.54	0.9382	2.08	0.9812
0.05	0.5199	0.55	0.7088	1.05	0.8531	1.55	0.9394	2.10	0.9821
0.06	0.5239	0.56	0.7123	1.06	0.8554	1.56	0.9406	2.12	0.9830
0.07	0.5279	0.57	0.7157	1.07	0.8577	1.57	0.9418	2.14	0.9838
0.08	0.5319	0.58	0.7190	1.08	0.8599	1.58	0.9429	2.16	0.9846
0.09	0.5359	0.59	0.7224	1.09	0.8621	1.59	0.9441	2.18	0.9854
0.10	0.5398	0.60	0.7257	1.10	0.8643	1.60	0.9452	2.20	0.9861
0.11	0.5438	0.61	0.7291	1.11	0.8665	1.61	0.9463	2.22	0.9868
0.12	0.5478	0.62	0.7324	1.12	0.8686	1.62	0.9474	2.24	0.9875
0.13	0.5517	0.63	0.7357	1.13	0.8708	1.63	0.9484	2.26	0.9881
0.14	0.5557	0.64	0.7389	1.14	0.8729	1.64	0.9495	2.28	0.9887
0.15	0.5596	0.65	0.7422	1.15	0.8749	1.65	0.9505	2.30	0.9893
0.16	0.5636	0.66	0.7454	1.16	0.8770	1.66	0.9515	2.32	0.9898
0.17	0.5675	0.67	0.7486	1.17	0.8790	1.67	0.9525	2.34	0.9904
0.18	0.5714	0.68	0.7517	1.18	0.8810	1.68	0.9535	2.36	0.9909
0.19	0.5753	0.69	0.7549	1.19	0.8830	1.69	0.9545	2.38	0.9913
0.20	0.5793	0.70	0.7580	1.20	0.8849	1.70	0.9554	2.40	0.9918
0.21	0.5832	0.71	0.7611	1.21	0.8869	1.71	0.9564	2.42	0.9922
0.22	0.5871	0.72	0.7642	1.22	0.8888	1.72	0.9573	2.44	0.9927
0.23	0.5910	0.73	0.7673	1.23	0.8907	1.73	0.9582	2.46	0.9931
0.24	0.5948	0.74	0.7704	1.24	0.8925	1.74	0.9591	2.48	0.9934
0.25	0.5987	0.75	0.7734	1.25	0.8944	1.75	0.9599	2.50	0.9938
0.26	0.6026	0.76	0.7764	1.26	0.8962	1.76	0.9608	2.55	0.9946
0.27	0.6064	0.77	0.7794	1.27	0.8980	1.77	0.9616	2.60	0.9953
0.28	0.6103	0.78	0.7823	1.28	0.8997	1.78	0.9625	2.65	0.9960
0.29	0.6141	0.79	0.7852	1.29	0.9015	1.79	0.9633	2.70	0.9965
0.30	0.6179	0.80	0.7881	1.30	0.9032	1.80	0.9641	2.75	0.9970
0.31	0.6217	0.81	0.7910	1.31	0.9049	1.81	0.9649	2.80	0.9974
0.32	0.6255	0.82	0.7939	1.32	0.9066	1.82	0.9656	2.85	0.9978
0.33	0.6293	0.83	0.7967	1.33	0.9082	1.83	0.9664	2.90	0.9981
0.34	0.6331	0.84	0.7995	1.34	0.9099	1.84	0.9671	2.95	0.9984
0.35	0.6368	0.85	0.8023	1.35	0.9115	1.85	0.9678	3.00	0.9987
0.36	0.6406	0.86	0.8051	1.36	0.9131	1.86	0.9686	3.05	0.9989
0.37	0.6443	0.87	0.8078	1.37	0.9147	1.87	0.9693	3.10	0.9990
0.38	0.6480	0.88	0.8106	1.38	0.9162	1.88	0.9699	3.15	0.9992
0.39	0.6517	0.89	0.8133	1.39	0.9177	1.89	0.9706	3.20	0.9993
0.40	0.6554	0.90	0.8159	1.40	0.9192	1.90	0.9713	3.25	0.9994
0.41	0.6591	0.91	0.8186	1.41	0.9207	1.91	0.9719	3.30	0.9995
0.42	0.6628	0.92	0.8212	1.42	0.9222	1.92	0.9726	3.35	0.9996
0.43	0.6664	0.93	0.8238	1.43	0.9236	1.93	0.9732	3.40	0.9997
0.44	0.6700	0.94	0.8264	1.44	0.9251	1.94	0.9738	3.50	0.9998
0.45	0.6736	0.95	0.8289	1.45	0.9265	1.95	0.9744	3.60	0.9998
0.46	0.6772	0.96	0.8315	1.46	0.9279	1.96	0.9750	3.70	0.9999
0.47	0.6808	0.97	0.8340	1.47	0.9292	1.97	0.9756	3.80	0.9999
0.48	0.6844	0.98	0.8365	1.48	0.9306	1.98	0.9761	3.90	1.0000
0.49	0.6879	0.99	0.8389	1.49	0.9319	1.99	0.9767	4.00	1.0000
0.50	0.6915	1.00	0.8413	1.50	0.9332	2.00	0.9772		

Percentage Points of the Normal Distribution

The values z in the table are those which a random variable $Z \sim N(0, 1)$ exceeds with probability p; that is, $P(Z > z) = 1 - \Phi(z) = p$.

p	z	p	z
0.5000	0.0000	0.0500	1.6449
0.4000	0.2533	0.0250	1.9600
0.3000	0.5244	0.0100	2.3263
0.2000	0.8416	0.0050	2.5758
0.1500	1.0364	0.0010	3.0902
0.1000	1.2816	0.0005	3.2905

Binomial Cumulative Distribution Function

The tabulated value is $P(X \leqslant x)$, where X has a binomial distribution with index n and parameter p.

$p =$	0.05	0.10	0.15	0.20	0.25	0.30	0.35	0.40	0.45	0.50
$n = 5, x = 0$	0.7738	0.5905	0.4437	0.3277	0.2373	0.1681	0.1160	0.0778	0.0503	0.0312
1	0.9774	0.9185	0.8352	0.7373	0.6328	0.5282	0.4284	0.3370	0.2562	0.1875
2	0.9988	0.9914	0.9734	0.9421	0.8965	0.8369	0.7648	0.6826	0.5931	0.5000
3	1.0000	0.9995	0.9978	0.9933	0.9844	0.9692	0.9460	0.9130	0.8688	0.8125
4	1.0000	1.0000	0.9999	0.9997	0.9990	0.9976	0.9947	0.9898	0.9815	0.9688
$n = 6, x = 0$	0.7351	0.5314	0.3771	0.2621	0.1780	0.1176	0.0754	0.0467	0.0277	0.0156
1	0.9672	0.8857	0.7765	0.6554	0.5339	0.4202	0.3191	0.2333	0.1636	0.1094
2	0.9978	0.9842	0.9527	0.9011	0.8306	0.7443	0.6471	0.5443	0.4415	0.3438
3	0.9999	0.9987	0.9941	0.9830	0.9624	0.9295	0.8826	0.8208	0.7447	0.6563
4	1.0000	0.9999	0.9996	0.9984	0.9954	0.9891	0.9777	0.9590	0.9308	0.8906
5	1.0000	1.0000	1.0000	0.9999	0.9998	0.9993	0.9982	0.9959	0.9917	0.9844
$n = 7, x = 0$	0.6983	0.4783	0.3206	0.2097	0.1335	0.0824	0.0490	0.0280	0.0152	0.0078
1	0.9556	0.8503	0.7166	0.5767	0.4449	0.3294	0.2338	0.1586	0.1024	0.0625
2	0.9962	0.9743	0.9262	0.8520	0.7564	0.6471	0.5323	0.4199	0.3164	0.2266
3	0.9998	0.9973	0.9879	0.9667	0.9294	0.8740	0.8002	0.7102	0.6083	0.5000
4	1.0000	0.9998	0.9988	0.9953	0.9871	0.9712	0.9444	0.9037	0.8471	0.7734
5	1.0000	1.0000	0.9999	0.9996	0.9987	0.9962	0.9910	0.9812	0.9643	0.9375
6	1.0000	1.0000	1.0000	1.0000	0.9999	0.9998	0.9994	0.9984	0.9963	0.9922
$n = 8, x = 0$	0.6634	0.4305	0.2725	0.1678	0.1001	0.0576	0.0319	0.0168	0.0084	0.0039
1	0.9428	0.8131	0.6572	0.5033	0.3671	0.2553	0.1691	0.1064	0.0632	0.0352
2	0.9942	0.9619	0.8948	0.7969	0.6785	0.5518	0.4278	0.3154	0.2201	0.1445
3	0.9996	0.9950	0.9786	0.9437	0.8862	0.8059	0.7064	0.5941	0.4770	0.3633
4	1.0000	0.9996	0.9971	0.9896	0.9727	0.9420	0.8939	0.8263	0.7396	0.6367
5	1.0000	1.0000	0.9998	0.9988	0.9958	0.9887	0.9747	0.9502	0.9115	0.8555
6	1.0000	1.0000	1.0000	0.9999	0.9996	0.9987	0.9964	0.9915	0.9819	0.9648
7	1.0000	1.0000	1.0000	1.0000	1.0000	0.9999	0.9998	0.9993	0.9983	0.9961
$n = 9, x = 0$	0.6302	0.3874	0.2316	0.1342	0.0751	0.0404	0.0207	0.0101	0.0046	0.0020
1	0.9288	0.7748	0.5995	0.4362	0.3003	0.1960	0.1211	0.0705	0.0385	0.0195
2	0.9916	0.9470	0.8591	0.7382	0.6007	0.4628	0.3373	0.2318	0.1495	0.0898
3	0.9994	0.9917	0.9661	0.9144	0.8343	0.7297	0.6089	0.4826	0.3614	0.2539
4	1.0000	0.9991	0.9944	0.9804	0.9511	0.9012	0.8283	0.7334	0.6214	0.5000
5	1.0000	0.9999	0.9994	0.9969	0.9900	0.9747	0.9464	0.9006	0.8342	0.7461
6	1.0000	1.0000	1.0000	0.9997	0.9987	0.9957	0.9888	0.9750	0.9502	0.9102
7	1.0000	1.0000	1.0000	1.0000	0.9999	0.9996	0.9986	0.9962	0.9909	0.9805
8	1.0000	1.0000	1.0000	1.0000	1.0000	1.0000	0.9999	0.9997	0.9992	0.9980
$n = 10, x = 0$	0.5987	0.3487	0.1969	0.1074	0.0563	0.0282	0.0135	0.0060	0.0025	0.0010
1	0.9139	0.7361	0.5443	0.3758	0.2440	0.1493	0.0860	0.0464	0.0233	0.0107
2	0.9885	0.9298	0.8202	0.6778	0.5256	0.3828	0.2616	0.1673	0.0996	0.0547
3	0.9990	0.9872	0.9500	0.8791	0.7759	0.6496	0.5138	0.3823	0.2660	0.1719
4	0.9999	0.9984	0.9901	0.9672	0.9219	0.8497	0.7515	0.6331	0.5044	0.3770
5	1.0000	0.9999	0.9986	0.9936	0.9803	0.9527	0.9051	0.8338	0.7384	0.6230
6	1.0000	1.0000	0.9999	0.9991	0.9965	0.9894	0.9740	0.9452	0.8980	0.8281
7	1.0000	1.0000	1.0000	0.9999	0.9996	0.9984	0.9952	0.9877	0.9726	0.9453
8	1.0000	1.0000	1.0000	1.0000	1.0000	0.9999	0.9995	0.9983	0.9955	0.9893
9	1.0000	1.0000	1.0000	1.0000	1.0000	1.0000	1.0000	0.9999	0.9997	0.9990

$p =$	0.05	0.10	0.15	0.20	0.25	0.30	0.35	0.40	0.45	0.50
$n = 12, x = 0$	0.5404	0.2824	0.1422	0.0687	0.0317	0.0138	0.0057	0.0022	0.0008	0.0002
1	0.8816	0.6590	0.4435	0.2749	0.1584	0.0850	0.0424	0.0196	0.0083	0.0032
2	0.9804	0.8891	0.7358	0.5583	0.3907	0.2528	0.1513	0.0834	0.0421	0.0193
3	0.9978	0.9744	0.9078	0.7946	0.6488	0.4925	0.3467	0.2253	0.1345	0.0730
4	0.9998	0.9957	0.9761	0.9274	0.8424	0.7237	0.5833	0.4382	0.3044	0.1938
5	1.0000	0.9995	0.9954	0.9806	0.9456	0.8822	0.7873	0.6652	0.5269	0.3872
6	1.0000	0.9999	0.9993	0.9961	0.9857	0.9614	0.9154	0.8418	0.7393	0.6128
7	1.0000	1.0000	0.9999	0.9994	0.9972	0.9905	0.9745	0.9427	0.8883	0.8062
8	1.0000	1.0000	1.0000	0.9999	0.9996	0.9983	0.9944	0.9847	0.9644	0.9270
9	1.0000	1.0000	1.0000	1.0000	1.0000	0.9998	0.9992	0.9972	0.9921	0.9807
10	1.0000	1.0000	1.0000	1.0000	1.0000	1.0000	0.9999	0.9997	0.9989	0.9968
11	1.0000	1.0000	1.0000	1.0000	1.0000	1.0000	1.0000	1.0000	0.9999	0.9998
$n = 15, x = 0$	0.4633	0.2059	0.0874	0.0352	0.0134	0.0047	0.0016	0.0005	0.0001	0.0000
1	0.8290	0.5490	0.3186	0.1671	0.0802	0.0353	0.0142	0.0052	0.0017	0.0005
2	0.9638	0.8159	0.6042	0.3980	0.2361	0.1268	0.0617	0.0271	0.0107	0.0037
3	0.9945	0.9444	0.8227	0.6482	0.4613	0.2969	0.1727	0.0905	0.0424	0.0176
4	0.9994	0.9873	0.9383	0.8358	0.6865	0.5155	0.3519	0.2173	0.1204	0.0592
5	0.9999	0.9978	0.9832	0.9389	0.8516	0.7216	0.5643	0.4032	0.2608	0.1509
6	1.0000	0.9997	0.9964	0.9819	0.9434	0.8689	0.7548	0.6098	0.4522	0.3036
7	1.0000	1.0000	0.9994	0.9958	0.9827	0.9500	0.8868	0.7869	0.6535	0.5000
8	1.0000	1.0000	0.9999	0.9992	0.9958	0.9848	0.9578	0.9050	0.8182	0.6964
9	1.0000	1.0000	1.0000	0.9999	0.9992	0.9963	0.9876	0.9662	0.9231	0.8491
10	1.0000	1.0000	1.0000	1.0000	0.9999	0.9993	0.9972	0.9907	0.9745	0.9408
11	1.0000	1.0000	1.0000	1.0000	1.0000	0.9999	0.9995	0.9981	0.9937	0.9824
12	1.0000	1.0000	1.0000	1.0000	1.0000	1.0000	0.9999	0.9997	0.9989	0.9963
13	1.0000	1.0000	1.0000	1.0000	1.0000	1.0000	1.0000	1.0000	0.9999	0.9995
14	1.0000	1.0000	1.0000	1.0000	1.0000	1.0000	1.0000	1.0000	1.0000	1.0000
$n = 20, x = 0$	0.3585	0.1216	0.0388	0.0115	0.0032	0.0008	0.0002	0.0000	0.0000	0.0000
1	0.7358	0.3917	0.1756	0.0692	0.0243	0.0076	0.0021	0.0005	0.0001	0.0000
2	0.9245	0.6769	0.4049	0.2061	0.0913	0.0355	0.0121	0.0036	0.0009	0.0002
3	0.9841	0.8670	0.6477	0.4114	0.2252	0.1071	0.0444	0.0160	0.0049	0.0013
4	0.9974	0.9568	0.8298	0.6296	0.4148	0.2375	0.1182	0.0510	0.0189	0.0059
5	0.9997	0.9887	0.9327	0.8042	0.6172	0.4164	0.2454	0.1256	0.0553	0.0207
6	1.0000	0.9976	0.9781	0.9133	0.7858	0.6080	0.4166	0.2500	0.1299	0.0577
7	1.0000	0.9996	0.9941	0.9679	0.8982	0.7723	0.6010	0.4159	0.2520	0.1316
8	1.0000	0.9999	0.9987	0.9900	0.9591	0.8867	0.7624	0.5956	0.4143	0.2517
9	1.0000	1.0000	0.9998	0.9974	0.9861	0.9520	0.8782	0.7553	0.5914	0.4119
10	1.0000	1.0000	1.0000	0.9994	0.9961	0.9829	0.9468	0.8725	0.7507	0.5881
11	1.0000	1.0000	1.0000	0.9999	0.9991	0.9949	0.9804	0.9435	0.8692	0.7483
12	1.0000	1.0000	1.0000	1.0000	0.9998	0.9987	0.9940	0.9790	0.9420	0.8684
13	1.0000	1.0000	1.0000	1.0000	1.0000	0.9997	0.9985	0.9935	0.9786	0.9423
14	1.0000	1.0000	1.0000	1.0000	1.0000	1.0000	0.9997	0.9984	0.9936	0.9793
15	1.0000	1.0000	1.0000	1.0000	1.0000	1.0000	1.0000	0.9997	0.9985	0.9941
16	1.0000	1.0000	1.0000	1.0000	1.0000	1.0000	1.0000	1.0000	0.9997	0.9987
17	1.0000	1.0000	1.0000	1.0000	1.0000	1.0000	1.0000	1.0000	1.0000	0.9998
18	1.0000	1.0000	1.0000	1.0000	1.0000	1.0000	1.0000	1.0000	1.0000	1.0000

$p =$	0.05	0.10	0.15	0.20	0.25	0.30	0.35	0.40	0.45	0.50
$n = 40, x = 0$	0.1285	0.0148	0.0015	0.0001	0.0000	0.0000	0.0000	0.0000	0.0000	0.0000
1	0.3991	0.0805	0.0121	0.0015	0.0001	0.0000	0.0000	0.0000	0.0000	0.0000
2	0.6767	0.2228	0.0486	0.0079	0.0010	0.0001	0.0000	0.0000	0.0000	0.0000
3	0.8619	0.4231	0.1302	0.0285	0.0047	0.0006	0.0001	0.0000	0.0000	0.0000
4	0.9520	0.6290	0.2633	0.0759	0.0160	0.0026	0.0003	0.0000	0.0000	0.0000
5	0.9861	0.7937	0.4325	0.1613	0.0433	0.0086	0.0013	0.0001	0.0000	0.0000
6	0.9966	0.9005	0.6067	0.2859	0.0962	0.0238	0.0044	0.0006	0.0001	0.0000
7	0.9993	0.9581	0.7559	0.4371	0.1820	0.0553	0.0124	0.0021	0.0002	0.0000
8	0.9999	0.9845	0.8646	0.5931	0.2998	0.1110	0.0303	0.0061	0.0009	0.0001
9	1.0000	0.9949	0.9328	0.7318	0.4395	0.1959	0.0644	0.0156	0.0027	0.0003
10	1.0000	0.9985	0.9701	0.8392	0.5839	0.3087	0.1215	0.0352	0.0074	0.0011
11	1.0000	0.9996	0.9880	0.9125	0.7151	0.4406	0.2053	0.0709	0.0179	0.0032
12	1.0000	0.9999	0.9957	0.9568	0.8209	0.5772	0.3143	0.1285	0.0386	0.0083
13	1.0000	1.0000	0.9986	0.9806	0.8968	0.7032	0.4408	0.2112	0.0751	0.0192
14	1.0000	1.0000	0.9996	0.9921	0.9456	0.8074	0.5721	0.3174	0.1326	0.0403
15	1.0000	1.0000	0.9999	0.9971	0.9738	0.8849	0.6946	0.4402	0.2142	0.0769
16	1.0000	1.0000	1.0000	0.9990	0.9884	0.9367	0.7978	0.5681	0.3185	0.1341
17	1.0000	1.0000	1.0000	0.9997	0.9953	0.9680	0.8761	0.6885	0.4391	0.2148
18	1.0000	1.0000	1.0000	0.9999	0.9983	0.9852	0.9301	0.7911	0.5651	0.3179
19	1.0000	1.0000	1.0000	1.0000	0.9994	0.9937	0.9637	0.8702	0.6844	0.4373
20	1.0000	1.0000	1.0000	1.0000	0.9998	0.9976	0.9827	0.9256	0.7870	0.5627
21	1.0000	1.0000	1.0000	1.0000	1.0000	0.9991	0.9925	0.9608	0.8669	0.6821
22	1.0000	1.0000	1.0000	1.0000	1.0000	0.9997	0.9970	0.9811	0.9233	0.7852
23	1.0000	1.0000	1.0000	1.0000	1.0000	0.9999	0.9989	0.9917	0.9595	0.8659
24	1.0000	1.0000	1.0000	1.0000	1.0000	1.0000	0.9996	0.9966	0.9804	0.9231
25	1.0000	1.0000	1.0000	1.0000	1.0000	1.0000	0.9999	0.9988	0.9914	0.9597
26	1.0000	1.0000	1.0000	1.0000	1.0000	1.0000	1.0000	0.9996	0.9966	0.9808
27	1.0000	1.0000	1.0000	1.0000	1.0000	1.0000	1.0000	0.9999	0.9988	0.9917
28	1.0000	1.0000	1.0000	1.0000	1.0000	1.0000	1.0000	1.0000	0.9996	0.9968
29	1.0000	1.0000	1.0000	1.0000	1.0000	1.0000	1.0000	1.0000	0.9999	0.9989
30	1.0000	1.0000	1.0000	1.0000	1.0000	1.0000	1.0000	1.0000	1.0000	0.9997
31	1.0000	1.0000	1.0000	1.0000	1.0000	1.0000	1.0000	1.0000	1.0000	0.9999
32	1.0000	1.0000	1.0000	1.0000	1.0000	1.0000	1.0000	1.0000	1.0000	1.0000

$p =$	0.05	0.10	0.15	0.20	0.25	0.30	0.35	0.40	0.45	0.50
$n = 50, x = 0$	0.0769	0.0052	0.0003	0.0000	0.0000	0.0000	0.0000	0.0000	0.0000	0.0000
1	0.2794	0.0338	0.0029	0.0002	0.0000	0.0000	0.0000	0.0000	0.0000	0.0000
2	0.5405	0.1117	0.0142	0.0013	0.0001	0.0000	0.0000	0.0000	0.0000	0.0000
3	0.7604	0.2503	0.0460	0.0057	0.0005	0.0000	0.0000	0.0000	0.0000	0.0000
4	0.8964	0.4312	0.1121	0.0185	0.0021	0.0002	0.0000	0.0000	0.0000	0.0000
5	0.9622	0.6161	0.2194	0.0480	0.0070	0.0007	0.0001	0.0000	0.0000	0.0000
6	0.9882	0.7702	0.3613	0.1034	0.0194	0.0025	0.0002	0.0000	0.0000	0.0000
7	0.9968	0.8779	0.5188	0.1904	0.0453	0.0073	0.0008	0.0001	0.0000	0.0000
8	0.9992	0.9421	0.6681	0.3073	0.0916	0.0183	0.0025	0.0002	0.0000	0.0000
9	0.9998	0.9755	0.7911	0.4437	0.1637	0.0402	0.0067	0.0008	0.0001	0.0000
10	1.0000	0.9906	0.8801	0.5836	0.2622	0.0789	0.0160	0.0022	0.0002	0.0000
11	1.0000	0.9968	0.9372	0.7107	0.3816	0.1390	0.0342	0.0057	0.0006	0.0000
12	1.0000	0.9990	0.9699	0.8139	0.5110	0.2229	0.0661	0.0133	0.0018	0.0002
13	1.0000	0.9997	0.9868	0.8894	0.6370	0.3279	0.1163	0.0280	0.0045	0.0005
14	1.0000	0.9999	0.9947	0.9393	0.7481	0.4468	0.1878	0.0540	0.0104	0.0013
15	1.0000	1.0000	0.9981	0.9692	0.8369	0.5692	0.2801	0.0955	0.0220	0.0033
16	1.0000	1.0000	0.9993	0.9856	0.9017	0.6839	0.3889	0.1561	0.0427	0.0077
17	1.0000	1.0000	0.9998	0.9937	0.9449	0.7822	0.5060	0.2369	0.0765	0.0164
18	1.0000	1.0000	0.9999	0.9975	0.9713	0.8594	0.6216	0.3356	0.1273	0.0325
19	1.0000	1.0000	1.0000	0.9991	0.9861	0.9152	0.7264	0.4465	0.1974	0.0595
20	1.0000	1.0000	1.0000	0.9997	0.9937	0.9522	0.8139	0.5610	0.2862	0.1013
21	1.0000	1.0000	1.0000	0.9999	0.9974	0.9749	0.8813	0.6701	0.3900	0.1611
22	1.0000	1.0000	1.0000	1.0000	0.9990	0.9877	0.9290	0.7660	0.5019	0.2399
23	1.0000	1.0000	1.0000	1.0000	0.9996	0.9944	0.9604	0.8438	0.6134	0.3359
24	1.0000	1.0000	1.0000	1.0000	0.9999	0.9976	0.9793	0.9022	0.7160	0.4439
25	1.0000	1.0000	1.0000	1.0000	1.0000	0.9991	0.9900	0.9427	0.8034	0.5561
26	1.0000	1.0000	1.0000	1.0000	1.0000	0.9997	0.9955	0.9686	0.8721	0.6641
27	1.0000	1.0000	1.0000	1.0000	1.0000	0.9999	0.9981	0.9840	0.9220	0.7601
28	1.0000	1.0000	1.0000	1.0000	1.0000	1.0000	0.9993	0.9924	0.9556	0.8389
29	1.0000	1.0000	1.0000	1.0000	1.0000	1.0000	0.9997	0.9966	0.9765	0.8987
30	1.0000	1.0000	1.0000	1.0000	1.0000	1.0000	0.9999	0.9986	0.9884	0.9405
31	1.0000	1.0000	1.0000	1.0000	1.0000	1.0000	1.0000	0.9995	0.9947	0.9675
32	1.0000	1.0000	1.0000	1.0000	1.0000	1.0000	1.0000	0.9998	0.9978	0.9836
33	1.0000	1.0000	1.0000	1.0000	1.0000	1.0000	1.0000	0.9999	0.9991	0.9923
34	1.0000	1.0000	1.0000	1.0000	1.0000	1.0000	1.0000	1.0000	0.9997	0.9967
35	1.0000	1.0000	1.0000	1.0000	1.0000	1.0000	1.0000	1.0000	0.9999	0.9987
36	1.0000	1.0000	1.0000	1.0000	1.0000	1.0000	1.0000	1.0000	1.0000	0.9995
37	1.0000	1.0000	1.0000	1.0000	1.0000	1.0000	1.0000	1.0000	1.0000	0.9998
38	1.0000	1.0000	1.0000	1.0000	1.0000	1.0000	1.0000	1.0000	1.0000	1.0000

Poisson Cumulative Distribution Function

The tabulated value is $P(X \leq x)$, where X has a Poisson distribution with parameter λ.

$\lambda =$	0.5	1.0	1.5	2.0	2.5	3.0	3.5	4.0	4.5	5.0
$x = 0$	0.6065	0.3679	0.2231	0.1353	0.0821	0.0498	0.0302	0.0183	0.0111	0.0067
1	0.9098	0.7358	0.5578	0.4060	0.2873	0.1991	0.1359	0.0916	0.0611	0.0404
2	0.9856	0.9197	0.8088	0.6767	0.5438	0.4232	0.3208	0.2381	0.1736	0.1247
3	0.9982	0.9810	0.9344	0.8571	0.7576	0.6472	0.5366	0.4335	0.3423	0.2650
4	0.9998	0.9963	0.9814	0.9473	0.8912	0.8153	0.7254	0.6288	0.5321	0.4405
5	1.0000	0.9994	0.9955	0.9834	0.9580	0.9161	0.8576	0.7851	0.7029	0.6160
6	1.0000	0.9999	0.9991	0.9955	0.9858	0.9665	0.9347	0.8893	0.8311	0.7622
7	1.0000	1.0000	0.9998	0.9989	0.9958	0.9881	0.9733	0.9489	0.9134	0.8666
8	1.0000	1.0000	1.0000	0.9998	0.9989	0.9962	0.9901	0.9786	0.9597	0.9319
9	1.0000	1.0000	1.0000	1.0000	0.9997	0.9989	0.9967	0.9919	0.9829	0.9682
10	1.0000	1.0000	1.0000	1.0000	0.9999	0.9997	0.9990	0.9972	0.9933	0.9863
11	1.0000	1.0000	1.0000	1.0000	1.0000	0.9999	0.9997	0.9991	0.9976	0.9945
12	1.0000	1.0000	1.0000	1.0000	1.0000	1.0000	0.9999	0.9997	0.9992	0.9980
13	1.0000	1.0000	1.0000	1.0000	1.0000	1.0000	1.0000	0.9999	0.9997	0.9993
14	1.0000	1.0000	1.0000	1.0000	1.0000	1.0000	1.0000	1.0000	0.9999	0.9998
15	1.0000	1.0000	1.0000	1.0000	1.0000	1.0000	1.0000	1.0000	1.0000	0.9999
16	1.0000	1.0000	1.0000	1.0000	1.0000	1.0000	1.0000	1.0000	1.0000	1.0000
17	1.0000	1.0000	1.0000	1.0000	1.0000	1.0000	1.0000	1.0000	1.0000	1.0000
18	1.0000	1.0000	1.0000	1.0000	1.0000	1.0000	1.0000	1.0000	1.0000	1.0000
19	1.0000	1.0000	1.0000	1.0000	1.0000	1.0000	1.0000	1.0000	1.0000	1.0000

$\lambda =$	5.5	6.0	6.5	7.0	7.5	8.0	8.5	9.0	9.5	10.0
$x = 0$	0.0041	0.0025	0.0015	0.0009	0.0006	0.0003	0.0002	0.0001	0.0001	0.0000
1	0.0266	0.0174	0.0113	0.0073	0.0047	0.0030	0.0019	0.0012	0.0008	0.0005
2	0.0884	0.0620	0.0430	0.0296	0.0203	0.0138	0.0093	0.0062	0.0042	0.0028
3	0.2017	0.1512	0.1118	0.0818	0.0591	0.0424	0.0301	0.0212	0.0149	0.0103
4	0.3575	0.2851	0.2237	0.1730	0.1321	0.0996	0.0744	0.0550	0.0403	0.0293
5	0.5289	0.4457	0.3690	0.3007	0.2414	0.1912	0.1496	0.1157	0.0885	0.0671
6	0.6860	0.6063	0.5265	0.4497	0.3782	0.3134	0.2562	0.2068	0.1649	0.1301
7	0.8095	0.7440	0.6728	0.5987	0.5246	0.4530	0.3856	0.3239	0.2687	0.2202
8	0.8944	0.8472	0.7916	0.7291	0.6620	0.5925	0.5231	0.4557	0.3918	0.3328
9	0.9462	0.9161	0.8774	0.8305	0.7764	0.7166	0.6530	0.5874	0.5218	0.4579
10	0.9747	0.9574	0.9332	0.9015	0.8622	0.8159	0.7634	0.7060	0.6453	0.5830
11	0.9890	0.9799	0.9661	0.9467	0.9208	0.8881	0.8487	0.8030	0.7520	0.6968
12	0.9955	0.9912	0.9840	0.9730	0.9573	0.9362	0.9091	0.8758	0.8364	0.7916
13	0.9983	0.9964	0.9929	0.9872	0.9784	0.9658	0.9486	0.9261	0.8981	0.8645
14	0.9994	0.9986	0.9970	0.9943	0.9897	0.9827	0.9726	0.9585	0.9400	0.9165
15	0.9998	0.9995	0.9988	0.9976	0.9954	0.9918	0.9862	0.9780	0.9665	0.9513
16	0.9999	0.9998	0.9996	0.9990	0.9980	0.9963	0.9934	0.9889	0.9823	0.9730
17	1.0000	0.9999	0.9998	0.9996	0.9992	0.9984	0.9970	0.9947	0.9911	0.9857
18	1.0000	1.0000	0.9999	0.9999	0.9997	0.9993	0.9987	0.9976	0.9957	0.9928
19	1.0000	1.0000	1.0000	1.0000	0.9999	0.9997	0.9995	0.9989	0.9980	0.9965
20	1.0000	1.0000	1.0000	1.0000	1.0000	0.9999	0.9998	0.9996	0.9991	0.9984
21	1.0000	1.0000	1.0000	1.0000	1.0000	1.0000	0.9999	0.9998	0.9996	0.9993
22	1.0000	1.0000	1.0000	1.0000	1.0000	1.0000	1.0000	0.9999	0.9999	0.9997

Percentage Points of the χ^2 Distribution Function

The values in the table are those which a random variable with the χ^2 distribution on v degrees of freedom exceeds with the probability shown.

v	0.995	0.990	0.975	0.950	0.900	0.100	0.050	0.025	0.010	0.005
1	0.000	0.000	0.001	0.004	0.016	2.705	3.841	5.024	6.635	7.879
2	0.010	0.020	0.051	0.103	0.211	4.605	5.991	7.378	9.210	10.597
3	0.072	0.115	0.216	0.352	0.584	6.251	7.815	9.348	11.345	12.838
4	0.207	0.297	0.484	0.711	1.064	7.779	9.488	11.143	13.277	14.860
5	0.412	0.554	0.831	1.145	1.610	9.236	11.070	12.832	15.086	16.750
6	0.676	0.872	1.237	1.635	2.204	10.645	12.592	14.449	16.812	18.548
7	0.989	1.239	1.690	2.167	2.833	12.017	14.067	16.013	18.475	20.278
8	1.344	1.646	2.180	2.733	3.490	13.362	15.507	17.535	20.090	21.955
9	1.735	2.088	2.700	3.325	4.168	14.684	16.919	19.023	21.666	23.589
10	2.156	2.558	3.247	3.940	4.865	15.987	18.307	20.483	23.209	25.188
11	2.603	3.053	3.816	4.575	5.580	17.275	19.675	21.920	24.725	26.757
12	3.074	3.571	4.404	5.226	6.304	18.549	21.026	23.337	26.217	28.300
13	3.565	4.107	5.009	5.892	7.042	19.812	22.362	24.736	27.688	29.819
14	4.075	4.660	5.629	6.571	7.790	21.064	23.685	26.119	29.141	31.319
15	4.601	5.229	6.262	7.261	8.547	22.307	24.996	27.488	30.578	32.801
16	5.142	5.812	6.908	7.962	9.312	23.542	26.296	28.845	32.000	34.267
17	5.697	6.408	7.564	8.672	10.085	24.769	27.587	30.191	33.409	35.718
18	6.265	7.015	8.231	9.390	10.865	25.989	28.869	31.526	34.805	37.156
19	6.844	7.633	8.907	10.117	11.651	27.204	30.144	32.852	36.191	38.582
20	7.434	8.260	9.591	10.851	12.443	28.412	31.410	34.170	37.566	39.997
21	8.034	8.897	10.283	11.591	13.240	29.615	32.671	35.479	38.932	41.401
22	8.643	9.542	10.982	12.338	14.042	30.813	33.924	36.781	40.289	42.796
23	9.260	10.196	11.689	13.091	14.848	32.007	35.172	38.076	41.638	44.181
24	9.886	10.856	12.401	13.848	15.659	33.196	36.415	39.364	42.980	45.558
25	10.520	11.524	13.120	14.611	16.473	34.382	37.652	40.646	44.314	46.928
26	11.160	12.198	13.844	15.379	17.292	35.563	38.885	41.923	45.642	48.290
27	11.808	12.879	14.573	16.151	18.114	36.741	40.113	43.194	46.963	49.645
28	12.461	13.565	15.308	16.928	18.939	37.916	41.337	44.461	48.278	50.993
29	13.121	14.256	16.047	17.708	19.768	39.088	42.557	45.722	49.588	52.336
30	13.787	14.953	16.791	18.493	20.599	40.256	43.773	46.979	50.892	53.672

Critical Values for Correlation Coefficients

These tables concern tests of the hypothesis that a population correlation coefficient ρ is 0.
The values in the tables are the minimum values which need to be reached by a sample correlation coefficient in order to be significant at the level shown, on a one-tailed test.

Product moment coefficient					Sample size	Spearman's coefficient		
Level						Level		
0.10	0.05	0.025	0.01	0.005		0.05	0.025	0.01
0.8000	0.9000	0.9500	0.9800	0.9900	4	1.0000	-	-
0.6870	0.8054	0.8783	0.9343	0.9587	5	0.9000	1.0000	1.0000
0.6084	0.7293	0.8114	0.8822	0.9172	6	0.8286	0.8857	0.9429
0.5509	0.6694	0.7545	0.8329	0.8745	7	0.7143	0.7857	0.8929
0.5067	0.6215	0.7067	0.7887	0.8343	8	0.6429	0.7381	0.8333
0.4716	0.5822	0.6664	0.7498	0.7977	9	0.6000	0.7000	0.7833
0.4428	0.5494	0.6319	0.7155	0.7646	10	0.5636	0.6485	0.7455
0.4187	0.5214	0.6021	0.6851	0.7348	11	0.5364	0.6182	0.7091
0.3981	0.4973	0.5760	0.6581	0.7079	12	0.5035	0.5874	0.6783
0.3802	0.4762	0.5529	0.6339	0.6835	13	0.4835	0.5604	0.6484
0.3646	0.4575	0.5324	0.6120	0.6614	14	0.4637	0.5385	0.6264
0.3507	0.4409	0.5140	0.5923	0.6411	15	0.4464	0.5214	0.6036
0.3383	0.4259	0.4973	0.5742	0.6226	16	0.4294	0.5029	0.5824
0.3271	0.4124	0.4821	0.5577	0.6055	17	0.4142	0.4877	0.5662
0.3170	0.4000	0.4683	0.5425	0.5897	18	0.4014	0.4716	0.5501
0.3077	0.3887	0.4555	0.5285	0.5751	19	0.3912	0.4596	0.5351
0.2992	0.3783	0.4438	0.5155	0.5614	20	0.3805	0.4466	0.5218
0.2914	0.3687	0.4329	0.5034	0.5487	21	0.3701	0.4364	0.5091
0.2841	0.3598	0.4227	0.4921	0.5368	22	0.3608	0.4252	0.4975
0.2774	0.3515	0.4133	0.4815	0.5256	23	0.3528	0.4160	0.4862
0.2711	0.3438	0.4044	0.4716	0.5151	24	0.3443	0.4070	0.4757
0.2653	0.3365	0.3961	0.4622	0.5052	25	0.3369	0.3977	0.4662
0.2598	0.3297	0.3882	0.4534	0.4958	26	0.3306	0.3901	0.4571
0.2546	0.3233	0.3809	0.4451	0.4869	27	0.3242	0.3828	0.4487
0.2497	0.3172	0.3739	0.4372	0.4785	28	0.3180	0.3755	0.4401
0.2451	0.3115	0.3673	0.4297	0.4705	29	0.3118	0.3685	0.4325
0.2407	0.3061	0.3610	0.4226	0.4629	30	0.3063	0.3624	0.4251
0.2070	0.2638	0.3120	0.3665	0.4026	40	0.2640	0.3128	0.3681
0.1843	0.2353	0.2787	0.3281	0.3610	50	0.2353	0.2791	0.3293
0.1678	0.2144	0.2542	0.2997	0.3301	60	0.2144	0.2545	0.3005
0.1550	0.1982	0.2352	0.2776	0.3060	70	0.1982	0.2354	0.2782
0.1448	0.1852	0.2199	0.2597	0.2864	80	0.1852	0.2201	0.2602
0.1364	0.1745	0.2072	0.2449	0.2702	90	0.1745	0.2074	0.2453
0.1292	0.1654	0.1966	0.2324	0.2565	100	0.1654	0.1967	0.2327

Random Numbers

86	13	84	10	07	30	39	05	97	96	88	07	37	26	04	89	13	48	19	20
60	78	48	12	99	47	09	46	91	33	17	21	03	94	79	00	08	50	40	16
78	48	06	37	82	26	01	06	64	65	94	41	17	26	74	66	61	93	24	97
80	56	90	79	66	94	18	40	97	79	93	20	41	51	25	04	20	71	76	04
99	09	39	25	66	31	70	56	30	15	52	17	87	55	31	11	10	68	98	23
56	32	32	72	91	65	97	36	56	61	12	79	95	17	57	16	53	58	96	36
66	02	49	93	97	44	99	15	56	86	80	57	11	78	40	23	58	40	86	14
31	77	53	94	05	93	56	14	71	23	60	46	05	33	23	72	93	10	81	23
98	79	72	43	14	76	54	77	66	29	84	09	88	56	75	86	41	67	04	42
50	97	92	15	10	01	57	01	87	33	73	17	70	18	40	21	24	20	66	62
90	51	94	50	12	48	88	95	09	34	09	30	22	27	25	56	40	76	01	59
31	99	52	24	13	43	27	88	11	39	41	65	00	84	13	06	31	79	74	97
22	96	23	34	46	12	67	11	48	06	99	24	14	83	78	37	65	73	39	47
06	84	55	41	27	06	74	59	14	29	20	14	45	75	31	16	05	41	22	96
08	64	89	30	25	25	71	35	33	31	04	56	12	67	03	74	07	16	49	32
86	87	62	43	15	11	76	49	79	13	78	80	93	89	09	57	07	14	40	74
94	44	97	13	77	04	35	02	12	76	60	91	93	40	81	06	85	85	72	84
63	25	55	14	66	47	99	90	02	90	83	43	16	01	19	69	11	78	87	16
11	22	83	98	15	21	18	57	53	42	91	91	26	52	89	13	86	00	47	61
01	70	10	83	94	71	13	67	11	12	36	54	53	32	90	43	79	01	95	15

GLOSSARY

alternative hypothesis (when doing a **hypothesis test**) tells you about the **parameter** if your **assumption** is proved wrong

approximate (**verb**) to also calculate something fairly accurately but not exactly

approximation, also **'approximate' (noun)** an estimate that is almost correct; usually found when it would take too long to find an exact answer

assumption something which you believe to be true

bias an argument in favour of one thing over another based on personal opinion, not fair judgement

binomial distribution a **distribution** where each trial has two outcomes: success and failure. The trials are **independent** and have a fixed probability of success

cell an entry in a table, used in **chi-squared** testing

census observes or measures every member of a population

chi-squared distribution a distribution used to measure how well **observed** data fits with expected data

class a grouping of values

classify to group things by type

component a part of a larger whole, especially that of a machine or vehicle.

confidence interval a range of values, defined so that there is a specific probability that the true value of the **parameter** lies within that range

consecutive occurring one after another

constant staying at the same level; a term that has no **variable**, e.g. the constant term in the expression $x^2 + 3x - 6$ is -6

constraint a rule about your data that reduces your **degrees of freedom** by one

contingency table a table showing the **distribution** of one **variable** in rows and another in columns

continuity correction used with a **continuous probability distribution** to **approximate** a discrete probability distribution

continuous data that can take any value in a given range

continuous random variable a **variable** that can take any value in a given range

continuous uniform distribution a continuous probability distribution which has a constant probability function

correlation a measure of how well two sets of data are related to each other

corresponding matching or related to

criteria plural of **criterion**

criterion a standard by which something is judged

critical region (in a **hypothesis test**) we reject the null hypothesis if the test **statistic** is in the critical region

critical value the first value to fall inside of the **critical region**

cumulative increasing in value by successive additions

defective faulty; not working correctly

degrees of freedom a measure of the amount of information from the **sample** data that has not been used up. Every time a **statistic** is calculated from a sample, one degree of freedom is used up

discrete data that can only take certain values in a given range

discrete random variable takes only countable values

distribution the way something is shared across a particular area or group

expectation the **mean** of a **random variable**

independent when one event has no effect on another

interval a period of time or space between two events; a range of values

linear correlation a measure used to understand the relationship between two variables

mean the sum of all the **observations** divided by the total number of observations

median a value which has 50% of the probability below it

mode highest value for the probability density function

model (**noun**) an example used to explain how something works

model (**verb**) to use **assumptions** to make a real-world example easier to understand

null hypothesis (when doing a **hypothesis test**) the assumption about the **parameter** you are going to make

observation something you have seen

outcome the result of an experiment

parameter a value from the population that describes the population

population parameter see **parameter**

probability a measure showing how likely it is that something will happen

proportional increasing or decreasing in amount or degree in relation to changes in something else

quota the limited number of something that is allowed

rank (noun) a number that shows the position of something on a scale in relation to other things

rank (verb) to give something a particular position on a scale in order to show its important in relation to other things on the scale

ranking the position of something on a scale showing its importance in relation to other things on the scale

random chosen by chance; without any regular pattern

restriction a rule that limits what can happen

sample a small representative set from a population

sampling distribution a **distribution** of the values that a **statistic** can take, along with their probabilities

sampling frame a list of **sampling units**

sampling unit the individual units of a population

satisfy to meet the requirements

significance level the probability of rejecting the **null hypothesis** in a **hypothesis test**

singly one at a time

statistic a function of the data from a **sample** only; it cannot contain any **parameters**

strata (plural of stratum) classes of data which are mutually exclusive based on a criterion

test statistic a value from **observations** which is used in a **hypothesis test**

theoretical distribution based on ideas rather than observed; something that is possible in theory

unbiased estimator a judgement made fairly; without **bias**

uniformly in a way that is the same in all parts

variable able to be changed. Represented by a symbol (X, Y, A, B etc.) and able to take on any of a specified set of values

variance a measure of how spread out the **distribution** is

ANSWERS

CHAPTER 1

Prior knowledge check

1 165

Exercise 1A

1 The selection of individual elements of a population. Advantages: low cost, results obtained faster than a census, represents whole population.

2 Every item is observed/measured, e.g. National census for forecasting social funding. Census of a nursery school for numbers of carriers of a virus.

3 All the ropes would be destroyed in testing them.

4 **a** Cheaper, quicker.
   b The sampling frame is a list of all the members in the population.
   c The larger the population, the longer the list, so the larger the sampling frame.

5 **a** 01, 06, 64, 65, 94, 41 or 01, 18, 70, 97 99, 56: others are possible.
   b 079, 056, 110, 086, 143, 108 or 136, 097, 148, 069, 137, 123; others possible.
   c 010, 441, 172, 193, 249, 569 or 010, 184, 561, 547, 570, 278.

Exercise 1B

1 **a** Year 1: 8, Year 2: 12, Year 3: 16
   b ANY ONE FROM: sample accurately reflects the population structure of the school; guarantees proportional representation of different year groups in the sample.

2 **a** Patterns in the sample data might occur when taking every 20th person.
   b A simple random sample using the alphabetical list as the sampling frame.

3 **a** No: A systematic sample requires the first selected person to be chosen at random.
   b Take a simple random sample using the list of members as the sampling frame.

4 **a** Stratified sampling.
   b Male Y12: 10, Male Y13: 7, Female Y12: 12, Female Y13: 11

5 $k = \dfrac{480}{30} = 16$

Randomly select a number between 1 and 16. Starting with the worker with this clocking-in number, select the workers that have every 16th clocking-in number after this.

6 **a** Any method in which every member of the population has an equal chance of being selected, e.g. lottery. Disadvantage: the sample may not accurately reflect the proportions of members at the club who play each sport.
   b The sample will have proportional representation of the members who play the different sports.
   c Tennis: 10, Badminton: 12, Squash: 8

Exercise 1C

1 Divide the population into groups according to given characteristics. The size of each group determines the proportion of the sample that should have that characteristic. The interviewer assesses which group people fall into as part of the interview. Once a quota has been filled, no more people in that group are interviewed.

2 Similarities: The population is divided according to the characteristics of the whole population (into strata for stratified sampling, and groups for quota sampling) Differences: Stratified sampling uses random sampling whereas quota sampling does not.

3 **a** Sample is likely to be biased towards people who eat kebabs on a Friday.
   b Survey people at different times of day. Survey people in other parts of the town, not outside the kebab shop.

4 **a** 5.4 hours
   b Opportunity sampling; unlikely to provide a representative sample of the town as a whole
   c Increase the number of people asked. Ask people at different times/in different locations.

5 **a** Student's opportunity sample: For example, first five values
   b 1.9, 2.0, 2.6, 2.3, 2.0
   c 1.96 m, 2.16 m
   d Systematic sample – is random and likely to be more representative. Opportunity sample might get all the small values, for example.

Chapter review 1

1 **a** Sampling frame: first 15 days in January 2019
       Allocate each date a number from 1 to 15
       Use the random number function on calculator to generate 5 numbers between 1 and 15
   b Students' own answers.
   c 21.1°C

2 **a** **i** Advantage: very accurate; disadvantage: expensive (time consuming).
       ii Advantage: easier data collection (quick, cheap); disadvantage: possible bias.
   b Assign unique 3-digit identifiers 000, 001, ..., 499 to each member of the population. Work along rows of random number tables generating 3-digit numbers. If these correspond to an identifier then include the corresponding member in the sample; ignore repeats and numbers greater than 499. Repeat this process until the sample contains 100 members.

3 **a** **i** Collection of individual items.
       ii List of sampling units.
   b **i** List of registered owners from DVLC.
       ii List of people visiting a doctor's clinic in Oxford in July 1996.

4 **a** Advantage – the results are the most representative of the population since the structure of the sample reflects the structure of the population.
       Disadvantage – you need to know the structure of the population before you can take a stratified sample.
   b Advantage – quick and cheap.
       Disadvantage – can introduce bias (e.g. if the sample, by chance, only includes very tall people in an investigation into heights of students).

5 a Cabin crew not represented.
  b i Get a list of the 300 employees.
  $\frac{300}{30} = 10$ so choose one of the first 10 employees on the list at random and every subsequent 10th employee on the list, e.g. if person 7 is chosen, then the sample includes employees 7, 17, ..., 297.
  ii The population contains 100 pilots ($\frac{1}{3}$ of population) and 200 cabin crew ($\frac{2}{3}$ of population).
  The sample should contain $\frac{1}{3} \times 30 = 10$ pilots and $\frac{2}{3} \times 30 = 20$ cabin crew. The 10 pilots in the sample should be a simple random sample of the 100 pilots. The 20 cabin crew should be a simple random sample of the 200 cabin crew.
  iii Decide the categories e.g. age, gender, pilot or cabin crew and set a quota for each in proportion to their numbers in the population. Interview employees until quotas are full.

6 a Allocate a number between 1 and 120 to each student.
  Use random number tables, computer or calculator to select 15 different numbers between 1 and 120 (or equivalent).
  Students corresponding to these numbers become the sample.
  b Allocate numbers 1–64 to girls and 65–120 to boys.
  Select $\frac{64}{120} \times 15 = 8$ different random numbers between 1 and 64 for girls.
  Select 7 different random numbers between 65 and 120 for boys. Include the corresponding boys and girls in the sample.

7 a Stratified sampling.
  b Uses naturally occurring (strata) groupings. The results are more likely to represent the views of the population since the sample reflects its structure.

CHAPTER 2

Prior knowledge check

1 a 0.8944   **b** 0.2902
2 a 0.6745   **b** 1.0364
3 a 14   **b** 27   **c** −41

Exercise 2A

1 a $W \sim N(130, 13)$ **b** $W \sim N(30, 13)$
2 $R \sim N(148, 18)$
3 a $T \sim N(180, 225)$ or $N(180, 15^2)$
  b $T \sim N(350, 784)$ or $N(350, 28^2)$
  c $T \sim N(530, 1009)$
  d $T \sim N(-40, 89)$
4 a 0.909   **b** 0.0512   **c** 0.319
  d 0.0614   **e** 0.857   **f** 0.855
5 a 0.7881   **b** 0.2119   **c** 0.3400   **d** 0.2882
6 a 0.4497   **b** 0.0495
7 0.0385
8 0.0537

Chapter review 2

1 a $A \sim N(35, 9)$ or $N(35, 3^2)$ **b** $A \sim N(7, 6)$
  c $A \sim N(41, 41)$ **d** $A \sim N(84, 82)$
  e $A \sim N(19, 15)$
2 a 10   **b** 9   **c** 0.136
3 a 64   **b** 148   **c** 0.0293   **d** 28
4 a i 0.268   **ii** 0.436
  b 37.1 cm (3 s.f.)

5 a 0.3768   **b** 0.6226   **c** 0.9059
6 0.732
7 a i 60   **ii** 25
  b i $R \sim N(50, 20)$ **ii** 0.9320
8 a 0.8644
  b All random variables were independent – reasonable as games were chosen at random and game size and hard drive size are unconnected.
9 0.9044
10 a 0.7390   **b** 0.4018

Challenge

$\text{Var}(X + Y) = \text{E}((X + Y)^2) - (\text{E}(X + Y))^2$
$\qquad = \text{E}(X^2 + 2XY + Y^2) - (\text{E}(X) + \text{E}(Y))^2$
$\qquad = \text{E}(X^2) + 2\text{E}(X)\text{E}(Y) + \text{E}(Y^2) - (\text{E}(X^2))^2 -$
$\qquad\quad 2\text{E}(X)\text{E}(Y) - (\text{E}(Y))^2$
$\qquad = \text{E}(X^2) - (\text{E}(X))^2 + \text{E}(Y^2) - (\text{E}(Y))^2$
$\qquad = \text{Var}(X) + \text{Var}(Y)$

CHAPTER 3

Prior knowledge check

1 a 0.391   **b** $N(25, 45)$

Exercise 3A

1 i a $N(10\mu, 10\sigma^2)$ **b** $N(\mu, \frac{13}{25}\sigma^2)$
  c $N(0, 10\sigma^2)$ **d** $N\left(\mu, \frac{\sigma^2}{10}\right)$
  e $N(0, 10\sigma^2)$ **f** $N(0, 10)$
  ii a, b, d, e, are statistics since they do not contain μ or σ, the unknown population parameters.

2 a $\mu = \text{E}(x) = \frac{22}{5}$ or 4.4
  $\sigma^2 = 11.04$ or $\frac{276}{25}$
  b {1, 1} {1, 5}×2 {1, 10}×2
  {5, 5} {5, 10}×2
  {10, 10}
  c

$\overline{x}$	1	3	5	5.5	7.5	10
$P(\overline{X} = \overline{x})$	$\frac{4}{25}$	$\frac{8}{25}$	$\frac{4}{25}$	$\frac{4}{25}$	$\frac{4}{25}$	$\frac{1}{25}$

  e.g. $P(\overline{X} = 5.5) = \frac{4}{25}$
  d $\text{E}(\overline{X}) = 1 \times \frac{4}{25} + 3 \times \frac{8}{25} + \dots + 10 \times \frac{1}{25} = 4.4 = \mu$
  $\text{Var}(\overline{X}) = 1^2 \times \frac{4}{25} + 3^2 \times \frac{8}{25} + \dots + 10^2 \times \frac{1}{25} - 4.4^2$
  $\qquad = 5.52 = \frac{\sigma^2}{2}$

3 a $\overline{x} = 19.3$, $s^2 = 3.98$ **b** $\overline{x} = 3.375$, $s^2 = 4.65$
  c $\overline{x} = 223$, $s^2 = 7174$ **d** $\overline{x} = 0.5833$, $s^2 = 0.0269$
4 a 36.4, 29.2 (3 s.f.)   **b** 9, 4
  c 1.1, 0.0225   **d** 11.2, 2.24 (3 s.f.)
5 a An estimator of a population parameter that will 'on average' give the correct value.
  b $\overline{x} = 236$, $s^2 = 7.58$
6 a 0.0072
  b Sample taken from a population that was normally distributed, so answer is not an approximation.
7 a 0.2525   **b** 0.0098 ~ 0.0096
8 $\overline{x} = 205$ (3 s.f.), $s^2 = 9.22$ (3 s.f.)
9 a $\mu = \frac{20}{3}$, $\sigma^2 = \frac{50}{9}$
  b {5, 5, 5}
  {5, 5, 10}×3 {5, 10, 10}×3
  {10, 10, 10}
  c

$\overline{x}$	5	$\frac{20}{3}$	$\frac{25}{3}$	10
$P(\overline{X} = \overline{x})$	$\frac{8}{27}$	$\frac{12}{27}$	$\frac{6}{27}$	$\frac{1}{27}$

Online Worked solutions are available in SolutionBank.

d $E(\overline{X}) = \dfrac{20}{3} = \mu$, $Var(\overline{X}) = \dfrac{50}{27} = \dfrac{\sigma^2}{3}$

e

m	5	10
$P(M = m)$	$\frac{20}{27}$	$\frac{7}{27}$

f $E(M) = 6.296\ldots$
$Var(M) = 4.80\ldots$

g Bias = 1.30 (3 s.f.)

10 a $10p$

b $\overline{X} = \dfrac{X_1 + \ldots + X_{25}}{25}$

$E(\overline{X}) = \dfrac{E(X_1) + \ldots + E(X_{25})}{25} = \dfrac{25 \times 10p}{25} = 10p$

$\therefore \overline{X}$ is a biased estimator of p

so bias $= 10p - p = 9p$

c $\dfrac{\overline{X}}{10}$ is an unbiased estimator of p

11 a $E(X) = 0$

$\therefore \quad E(X^2) = \dfrac{\alpha^2}{3}$

b $Y = X_1^2 + X_2^2 + X_3^2$

$E(Y) = E(X_1^2) + E(X_2^2) + E(X_3^2) = \dfrac{\alpha^2}{3} \times 3 = \alpha^2$

$\therefore \; Y$ is an unbiased estimator of α^2

12 a $\overline{y} = 16.2$, $s_y^2 = 12.0$ (3 s.f.)

b $w = 15.92$, $s_w^2 = 10.34$

c Standard error is a measure of the statistical accuracy of an estimate.

d $\dfrac{s_x}{\sqrt{20}} = 0.632$ (3 s.f.), $\dfrac{s_y}{\sqrt{30}} = 0.633$ (3 s.f.),

$\dfrac{s_w}{\sqrt{50}} = 0.455$ (3 s.f.)

e Prefer to use w since it is based on a larger sample size and has smallest standard error.

13 a $\overline{x} = 65$, $s_x^2 = 9.74$ (3 s.f.)

b Need a sample of 37 or more

c No. Because the recommendation is based on the assumed value of s^2 from the original sample, or the value of s^2 for the new sample might be different/larger.

d 65.6 (3.s.f.)

14 Need a sample of 28 (or more)

15 a 4.89   **b** 0.0924 (3 s.f.)

c Need $n = 35$ (or more)

16 a $E(X_1) = np$, $E(X_2) = 2np$, $Var(X_1) = np(1 - p)$,
$Var(X_2) = 2np(1 - p)$

b Prefer $\dfrac{X_2}{2n}$ since based on larger sample
(and therefore will have smaller variance)

c $X = \dfrac{1}{2}\left(\dfrac{X_1}{n} + \dfrac{X_2}{2n}\right)$

$\Rightarrow E(X) = \dfrac{1}{2}\left(\dfrac{E(X_1)}{n} + \dfrac{E(X_2)}{2n}\right) = \dfrac{1}{2}\left(\dfrac{np}{n} + \dfrac{2np}{2n}\right)$

$= \dfrac{1}{2}(p + p) = p$

$\therefore \; X$ is an unbiased estimator of p

d $Y = \left(\dfrac{X_1 + X_2}{3n}\right)$

$\Rightarrow E(Y) = \dfrac{E(X_1) + E(X_2)}{3n} = \dfrac{np + 2np}{3n} = p$

$\therefore \; Y$ is an unbiased estimator of p

e $Var(Y)$ is smallest so Y is the best estimator.

f $\dfrac{p}{3}$

17 a $\mu = 1$, $\sigma^2 = 0.8$ or $\frac{4}{5}$

b {0, 0, 0}   {0, 0, 1}×3   {0, 0, 2}×3
{1, 1, 1}   {1, 1, 0}×3   {1, 1, 2}×3
{2, 2, 2}   {2, 2, 0}×3   {2, 2, 1}×3   {0, 1, 2}×3! = 6

c

$\overline{x}$	0	$\frac{1}{3}$	$\frac{2}{3}$	1	$\frac{4}{3}$	$\frac{5}{3}$	2
$P(\overline{X} = \overline{x})$	$\frac{8}{125}$	$\frac{12}{125}$	$\frac{30}{125}$	$\frac{25}{125}$	$\frac{30}{125}$	$\frac{12}{125}$	$\frac{8}{125}$

d $E(\overline{X}) = 1 (= \mu)$

$Var(\overline{X}) = \dfrac{4}{15} = \left(\dfrac{\sigma^2}{3}\right)$

e

n	0	1	2
$P(N = n)$	$\frac{44}{125}$	$\frac{37}{125}$	$\frac{44}{125}$

f $E(N) = 1$
$Var(N) = 0 + 1^2 \times \frac{37}{125} + 2^2 \times \frac{44}{125} - 1^2 = \frac{88}{125} (= \sigma^2)$

g $E(N) = 1 = \mu$

h $\overline{X}$ because $Var(\overline{X})$ is smaller.

Challenge

a $\dfrac{1}{n-1}\displaystyle\sum_{i=1}^{n}(x_i - \overline{x})^2 = \dfrac{S_{xx}}{n-1} = \dfrac{n}{n-1}\left(\dfrac{\sum x^2}{n} - \overline{x}^2\right)$

$= \dfrac{1}{n-1}\left(\sum x^2 - n\overline{x}^2\right)$

b $\sigma^2 = Var(X) = E(X^2) - \mu^2$

$E(X^2) = \sigma^2 + \mu^2$ (1)

$Var(\overline{X}) = \dfrac{\sigma^2}{n}$ and $E(\overline{X}) = \mu$

$\dfrac{\sigma^2}{n} = E(\overline{X}^2) - \mu^2$

$E(\overline{X}^2) = \dfrac{\sigma^2}{n} + \mu^2$ (2)

$S^2 = \dfrac{1}{n-1}\left(\sum X^2 - n\overline{X}^2\right)$

$E(S^2) = \dfrac{1}{n-1} E\left(\sum X^2 - n\overline{X}^2\right)$

$= \dfrac{1}{n-1}\left(E\left(\sum X^2\right) - nE(\overline{X}^2)\right)$

$E\left(\sum X^2\right) = \sum E(X^2) = nE(X^2)$

$E(S^2) = \dfrac{1}{n-1}\left(E(X^2) - nE(\overline{X}^2)\right)$

$= \dfrac{1}{n-1}\left(n(\sigma^2 + \mu^2) - n\left(\dfrac{\sigma^2}{n} + \mu^2\right)\right)$ by (1) and (2)

$= \sigma^2$

So the statistic S^2 is an unbiased estimator of the population variance σ^2, and s^2 is an unbiased estimate for σ^2.

Exercise 3B

1 a (124, 132)   **b** (123, 133)

2 a (83.7, 86.3)   **b** (83.4, 86.6)

3 (25.61, 27.19)

4 a $n = 609$ **b** $n = 865$ **c** $n = 1493$

5 a (304, 316) (3 s.f.)   **b** 0.0729

6 a Yes, Amy is correct. By the central limit theorem, for a large sample size, underlying population does not need to be normally distributed.

b (73 113, 78 631) (nearest integer)
or (73 100, 78 600) (3 s.f.)

7 a Must assume that these students form a random sample or that they are representative of the population.

b (66.7, 70.1)

c If $\mu = 65.3$ that is outside the C.I. so the examiner's sample was not representative. The examiner marked more better-than-average candidates.

8 a (23.2, 26.8) is 95% C.I. since it is the narrower interval.
  b 0.918   **c** 25
9 a (130, 140)   **b** 85%   **c** Need $n = 189$ or more
10 (30.4, 32.4) (3 s.f.)
11 (258, 274) (3 s.f.)
12 a 0.311   **b** 0.866   **c** (21.8, 23.3) (3 s.f.)

Chapter review 3

1 a $H_0: \mu = 0.48$, $H_1: \mu \neq 0.48$; Significance level = 10%; 0.48 is in confidence interval so accept H_0.
  b (0.4482, 0.5158)
2 a **i** and **iii** are since they only contain known data; **ii** is not since it contains unknown population parameters.
  b μ; $\dfrac{17\sigma^2}{9}$
3 a (46.7, 47.6) (3 s.f.)
  b Since the confidence interval is wholly above the value of 46.5, this suggests that the new supplier is correct in his claim.
4 a 4.53, 0.185 (3 d.p.)   **b** (4.10, 4.96) (3 s.f.)
  c 0.3520
5 14.01, 0.04 (2 d.p.)
6 The smallest value of n is 14.
7 a (41.1, 47.3) (3 s.f.)
  b t.s. = $-1.375 > -1.6449$
Not significant so accept H_0. There is insufficient evidence to support the headteachers' claim.
8 a $\bar{X} \sim N\left(\mu, \dfrac{\sigma^2}{n}\right)$
  b Exact because X is normally distributed.
  c Need $n = 28$ or more
9 a 0.75, 4.84
  b **i** assume that $\bar{X}$ has a normal distribution
    ii assume that the sample was random
  c $(-0.346, 1.85)$ (3 s.f.)
  d Since 0 is in the interval it is reasonable to assume that trains do arrive on time.
10 a $\bar{X} \sim N\left(\mu, \dfrac{\sigma^2}{n}\right)$
  b 95% C.I. is an interval within which we are 95% confident m lies.
  c (3.37, 14.1) (3 s.f.)
  d (9.07, 10.35) (nearest penny)
  e t.s. = $1.8769 > 1.6449$
Significant so reject H_0. There is evidence that the mean sales of unleaded fuel in 2010 were greater than in 2009.
  f $n = 163$
11 a A 98% C.I. is an interval within which we are 98% sure the population mean will lie.
  b 0.182 (3 d.p.)
  c (9.84, 10.56) (2 d. p.)
  d $n = 13$
12 a $E(\bar{X}) = \mu$, $Var(\bar{X}) = \dfrac{\sigma^2}{n}$
  b **i** $\bar{X} \sim N\left(\mu, \dfrac{\sigma^2}{n}\right)$ **ii** $\bar{X} \sim N\left(\mu, \dfrac{\sigma^2}{n}\right)$
  c (17.7, 19.3) (3 s.f.)
  d $n = 278$ or more
  e t.s. = $-2.1176 < -1.96$
Significant so reject H_0. There is evidence that the mean of till receipts in 2014 is different from the mean value in 2013.
13 a Approximately 83 samples will have mean < 0.823
  b (0.823, 0.845) (3 s.f.)
  c Since 0.824 is in the C.I. we can conclude that there is insufficient evidence of a fault.

14 a $H_0: \mu_d = \mu_w$; $H_1: \mu_d > \mu_w$; critical value is 2.6512 which is greater than the sig level (1.6449) so reject H_0 – doctor's claim is supported.
  b Assume normal distribution or assume sample sizes large enough to use the central limit theorem; Assume individual results are independent; Assume $\sigma^2 = s^2$ for both populations.
  c 58.5 (3 s.f.)

Challenge
a $T = r\bar{X} + s\bar{Y}$
$E(T) = r\mu + s\mu = (r + s)\mu$
So if T is unbiased then $r + s = 1$
b $r + s = 1 \Rightarrow s = 1 - r$
$\therefore T = r\bar{X} + (1 - r)\bar{Y}$
$Var(T) = r^2 Var(\bar{X}) + (1 - r)^2 Var(\bar{Y})$
$\qquad = r^2 \dfrac{\sigma^2}{n} + (1 - r)^2 \dfrac{\sigma^2}{m} = \sigma^2 \left(\dfrac{r^2}{n} + \dfrac{(1 - r)^2}{m}\right)$
c $\dfrac{d}{dr} Var(T) = \left(\sigma^2 \dfrac{2r}{n} + \dfrac{2(1 - r)(-1)}{m}\right)$
$\dfrac{d}{dr} Var(T) = 0 \Rightarrow rm = (1 - r)n \Rightarrow r(m + n) = n \Rightarrow r = \dfrac{n}{m + n}$
d $\dfrac{n\bar{X} + m\bar{Y}}{m + n}$

Review exercise 1

1 a A census observes every member of a population. Disadvantage: it would be time-consuming to get opinions from all the employees.
  b Opportunity sampling
  c Only cleaners – no managers i.e. not all types. Not a random sample; the first 50 may be in same shift/group/share same views.
  d **i** Label employees (1–550) or obtain an ordered list. Select first person using random numbers (from 1–11). Then select every 11th person from the list, e.g. if person 8 is selected then the sample is 8, 19, 30, 41, ...
    ii Label managers (1–55) and cleaners (1–495). Use random numbers to select 5 managers and 45 cleaners.
2 a Advantage – a sampling frame is not required
Disadvantage – sampling errors cannot be calculated
  b Advantage – very quick to administer
Disadvantage – may not be representative of the population
3 a 390 and 372
  b The list is alphabetical and has not been sorted by gender.
  c Stratified sampling
4 Label standard rooms between 1 and 180.
Use random numbers in the range 1–180 to select 18 rooms.
Label premier rooms between 1 and 100.
Use random numbers in the range 1–100 to select 10 rooms.
Label executive rooms between 1 and 40.
Use random numbers in the range 1–40 to select 4 rooms.
5 a 0.7586
  b The durations of the two rides are independent. This is likely to be the case as two separate control panels operate each of the rides.
  c $D \sim N(246, 27)$
  d 0.5713

Online Worked solutions are available in SolutionBank.

6 a 30 **b** 4.84 **c** 0.5764

7 $E\left(\dfrac{X_1 + X_2}{2} - \overline{X}\right) = 0$

$Var\left(\dfrac{X_1 + X_2}{2} - \overline{X}\right) = \dfrac{\sigma^2}{6}$

$k = 0.344$

8

$\overline{x}$	$P(\overline{X} = \overline{x})$
1	$\frac{20}{90}$
0.75	$\frac{30}{90}$
0.55	$\frac{20}{90}$
0.5	$\frac{6}{90}$
0.3	$\frac{12}{90}$
0.1	$\frac{2}{90}$

9 $\mu = 8.02$

10 0.754

11 a $E(\overline{X}) = 3\alpha - 6$, therefore a biased estimator with bias $\pm(2\alpha - 6)$
b $k = \frac{1}{3}$
c $\max(X) = 56.45$

12 a 0.7377 **b** 0.6858

13 a 0.9031 **b** 0.8811

14 a 0.1336 **b** 0.8413 **c** 0.1610
d All random variables are independent and normally distributed.

15 a $\overline{x} = 4.52$, $s^2 = 1.51$ (3 s.f.)
b $H_0: \mu_A = \mu_B$; $H_1: \mu_A > \mu_B$.
1.868... > 1.6449 so reject H_0. There is evidence that diet A is better than diet B or evidence that (mean) weight loss in the first week using diet A is more than with diet B.
c The central limit theorem enables you to assume that $\overline{A}$ and $\overline{B}$ are both normally distributed since both samples are large.
d Assumed $\sigma_A^2 = s_A^2$ and $\sigma_B^2 = s_B^2$

16 (127, 151) to 3 s.f.

17 a $\overline{x} = 50$, $s^2 = 0.193$ (3 s.f.)
b (49.7, 50.3)
c (49.6, 50.4)

18 a $\overline{x} = 110.5$, $s^2 = 672$ (3 s.f.)
b (95.0, 126) to 3.s.f.
c 0.4633 (4 d.p.)

19 a $\overline{x} = 168$, $s^2 = 27.0$ (3 s.f.)
b (166, 170) to 3 s.f.

20 a $\overline{x} = 287$, $s^2 = 7682.5$
b Sample size ($\geqslant$) 97 required.

21 a 0.0475 ($z = -1.67$)
b The weights of each slice are independent.

22 $n = 25$

23 a 14.6 **b** 85

Challenge

a $E\left(\frac{2}{3}X_1 - \frac{1}{2}X_2 + \frac{5}{6}X_3\right) = \frac{2}{3}\mu - \frac{1}{2}\mu + \frac{5}{6}\mu$
$E(Y) = \mu \Rightarrow$ unbiased

b $E(aX_1 + bX_2) = a\mu + b\mu = \mu$
$a + b = 1$
$Var(aX_1 + bX_2) = a^2\sigma^2 + b^2\sigma^2$
$= a^2\sigma^2 + (1 - a)^2\sigma^2 = (2a^2 - 2a + 1)\sigma^2$

c Minimum value when $(4a - 2)\sigma^2 = 0$
$\Rightarrow 4a - 2 = 0$
$a = \frac{1}{2}$, $b = \frac{1}{2}$

CHAPTER 4
Prior knowledge check

1 a $P(X > 115) = 1 - 0.2660 = 0.7340$
b $P(120 < X < 130) = 0.3944$
c $a = 114.60$

2 a −9.5 **b** $\frac{105}{4}$ **c** $\frac{2}{3}$

3 0.2744

Exercise 4A

1 a 0.0668 or 0.066807 **b** $n = 241$

2 0.1855

3 a 0.0416 **b** 0.0130

4 0.1103

5 a $k = 0.15$ **b** 0.1727
c Answer is an approximation, n is large, so fairly accurate.

6 Need n at least 1936

7 a Salaries are unlikely to be symetrically distributed so normal distribution would not be a good model.
b i 0.0231 **ii** 0.7804
c Estimate likely to be inaccurate, small sample size and unknown if original distribution was normal.

8 96

Exercise 4B

1 a 0.2084
b 0.1807, this estimate is inaccurate, sample size not big enough

2 0.9214

3 a 3.75 **b** 0.0748-9

4 a 0.1680 **b** 0.1587

5 $\overline{X} \sim N\left(2a + 1, \dfrac{(a + 4)^2}{120}\right)$

6 a 0.0019 **b** 0.0416

Exercise 4C

1 a (73 113, 78 631)
b Since n is large, the central limit theorem allows us to approximate the mean distance travelled as a normal distribution and so we can find a confidence interval for the mean distance travelled.

2 a $Var(X) = \dfrac{(b - a)^2}{12} = \dfrac{(\mu + 10 - (\mu - 10))}{12} = \dfrac{20^2}{12} = \dfrac{100}{3}$
b (77.7, 79.7)
c Since n is large, then the distribution of the sample mean will be normally distributed.

3 a (150.2, 199.8)
b It is not necessary to assume that the value of merchandise sold has a normal distribution because the sample size is large and we can use the central limit theorem.

4 a (14.15, 14.85)
b Maike should suggest that the supermarket reduces the stated fat content since the stated value of 15% is above the confidence interval.

5 a Since the sample size is large, the central limit theorem can approximate the sample mean as a normal distribution as the original distribution is not assumed to be normal.
b (1.76, 2.04)

6 a $\overline{Y} \sim N(a + 2, 0.4)$
b (20.41, 20.79)

Exercise 4D

1 Not significant. Accept H_0.
2 Significant. Reject H_0.
3 Not significant. Accept H_0.
4 Significant. Reject H_0.
5 Not significant. Accept H_0.
6 $\bar{X} < 119.39\ldots$ or 119 (3 s.f.)
7 $\bar{X} > 13.2$
8 $\bar{X} < 84.3$
9 $\bar{X} > 0.877$ or $\bar{X} < -0.877$
10 $\bar{X} > -7.31$ or $\bar{X} < -8.69$
11 Result is significant so reject H_0.
   There is evidence that the new formula is an improvement.
12 Result is significant so reject H_0.
   There is evidence to support the psychologist's theory.
13 $\sigma^2 = 0.15$, $n = 30$, $x = 8.95$
   H_0: $\mu = 9$ (no change)
   H_1: $\mu \neq 9$ (change in mean diameter)
   $Z = \dfrac{8.95 - 9}{0.15/\sqrt{30}} = -1.8257$ 5% C.I. is $Z = \pm 1.96$
   $-1.8257\ldots > -1.96$ so result is not significant.
   There is insufficient evidence of a change in mean diameter.

Exercise 4E

1 H_0: $\mu_1 = \mu_2$ H_1: $\mu_1 > \mu_2$ 5% c.v. is $z = 1.6449$
   t.s. $= Z = \dfrac{(23.8 - 21.5) - 0}{\sqrt{\frac{5^2}{15} + \frac{4.8^2}{20}}} = 1.3699\ldots$
   $1.3699 < 1.6449$ so result is not significant, accept H_0.
2 H_0: $\mu_1 = \mu_2$ H_1: $\mu_1 \neq \mu_2$ 5% c.v. is $z = \pm 1.96$
   t.s. $= Z = \dfrac{(51.7 - 49.6) - 0}{\sqrt{\frac{4.2^2}{30} + \frac{3.6^2}{25}}}$
   [Choose $\bar{x}_2 - \bar{x}_1$ to get $z > 0$]
   t.s. $Z = 1.996\ldots > 1.96$ so result is significant. Reject H_0.
3 H_0: $\mu_1 = \mu_2$ H_1: $\mu_1 < \mu_2$ 1% c.v. is $z = -2.3263$
   t.s. $= Z = \dfrac{(3.62 - 4.11) - 0}{\sqrt{\frac{0.81^2}{25} + \frac{0.75^2}{36}}} = -2.3946\ldots$
   t.s. $= -2.3946\ldots < -2.3263$ so result is significant
   Reject H_0.
4 H_0: $\mu_1 = \mu_2$ H_1: $\mu_1 \neq \mu_2$ 1% c.v. is $z = 2.5758$
   t.s. $= Z = \dfrac{(112.0 - 108.1) - 0}{\sqrt{\frac{8.2^2}{85} + \frac{11.3^2}{100}}} = 2.712\ldots > 2.5758$
   significant result so reject H_0.
   Central limit theorem applies since n_1, n_2 are large and enables you to assume $\bar{X}_1$ and $\bar{X}_2$ are both normally distributed.
5 H_0: $\mu_1 = \mu_2$ H_1: $\mu_1 > \mu_2$ 5% c.v. is $z = 1.96$
   t.s. $= Z = \dfrac{(72.6 - 69.5) - 0}{\sqrt{\frac{18.3^2}{100} + \frac{15.4^2}{150}}} = 1.396\ldots < 1.96$
   Result is not significant so accept H_0.
   Central limit theorem applies since n_1, n_2 are both large and enables you to assume $\bar{X}_1$ and $\bar{X}_2$ are normally distributed.
6 H_0: $\mu_1 = \mu_2$ H_1: $\mu_1 < \mu_2$ 1% c.v. is $z = -2.3263$
   t.s. $= Z = \dfrac{(0.863 - 0.868) - 0}{\sqrt{\frac{0.013^2}{120} + \frac{0.015^2}{90}}}$
   $= -2.5291\ldots < -2.3263$
   Result is significant so reject H_0.

Central limit theorem is used to assume $\bar{X}_1$ and $\bar{X}_2$ are normally distributed since both samples are large.
7 Not significant. There is insufficient evidence to suggest that the machines are producing pipes of different lengths.
8 **a** H_0: $\mu_{\text{new}} - \mu_{\text{old}} = 1$; H_1: $\mu_{\text{new}} - \mu_{\text{old}} > 1$
   Test statistic $= 3.668\ldots > $ c.v. (1.6449), therefore evidence that yes, the mean yield is more than 1 tonne greater.
   b Mean yield is normally distributed; Sample size is large.
9 **a** H_0: $\mu_{\text{grain}} - \mu_{\text{grain/grass}} = 0$; H_1: $\mu_{\text{grain}} \neq \mu_{\text{grain/grass}}$
   Test statistic $= 2.376\ldots > $ c.v. (1.96), therefore evidence that there is a difference between the mean fat content of the milk of cows fed on these two diets.
   b Mean fat content is normally distributed.

Challenge

a $\hat{\mu} = \dfrac{\sum\limits_1^{n_x} x_i + \sum\limits_1^{n_y} y_i}{\sum n} = \dfrac{n_x \bar{x} + n_y \bar{y}}{n_x + n_y}$

b (45.76, 47.33)

Exercise 4F

1 $2.34 > 1.6449$ so the result is significant.
   There is evidence that *Quickdry* dries faster than *Speedicover*.
2 **a** Not significant. There is insufficient evidence to confirm that mean expenditure in the week is more than at weekends.
   b We have assumed that $s_1 = \sigma_1$ and $s_2 = \sigma_2$.
3 **a** Not significant. Insufficient evidence to support a change in mean mass.
   b We have assumed that $s = \sigma$ since n is large.

Chapter review 4

1 0.0228
2 0.1855
3 $n \geqslant 3$
4 0.1030
5 **a** 0.1804 **b** 0.4191
6 **a** 0.9171
   b Sample taken from a population that was normally distributed, so answer is not an estimate.
   c 0.7009
7 0.8944
8 $n = 7$
9 0.0014
10 **a**

x	0	1
$P(X = x)$	0.4	0.6

$E(X) = 0.6$
$Var(X) = 0.24$

   b 0.1709
   c $n > 1025$
11 Test statistic $= 2.645$, critical value $= 1.6449$
   The result is significant, so reject H_0.
   There is evidence that the new bands are better.
12 Mean 14.01, standard error 0.04 (2 d.p.)
13 Test statistic $= -1.375$, critical value $= -1.6449$
   Not significant, so accept H_0. There is insufficient evidence to support the headteachers' claim.
14 Test statistic $= 1.8769$, critical value $= 1.6449$
   Significant, so reject H_0. There is evidence that the mean of all the 2010 unleaded fuel sales was greater than the mean of the 2009 sales.
15 **a** H_0: $\mu_d = \mu_w$; H_1: $\mu_d > \mu_w$; critical value is 2.6512 which is greater than the sig level (1.6449) so reject H_0 – the cardiologist's claim is supported.

Online Worked solutions are available in SolutionBank.

b Assume normal distribution or assume sample
sizes large enough to use the central limit theorem;
assume individual results are independent; assume
$\sigma_2 = s_2$ for both populations.

c 58.5 (3 s.f.)

Challenge

$X_1 + \dots + X_n \sim N(n\mu, n\sigma^2)$ and so

$\bar{X} = \frac{1}{n}(X_1 + \dots + X_n) \sim N\left(\frac{n\mu}{n}, \frac{n\sigma^2}{n^2}\right) = N\left(\mu, \frac{\sigma^2}{n}\right)$

CHAPTER 5

Prior knowledge check

1 a Strong negative correlation
  b As the age of the car goes up, the value goes down.
2 a 52   **b** 84   **c** 64

Exercise 5A

1 a The data clearly follows a linear trend.
  b Spearman's rank correlation coefficient is easier to
    calculate.
2 The relationship is clearly non-linear.
3 The number of attempts taken to score a free throw
  is not normally distributed (it is geometric) so the
  researcher should use Spearman's rank correlation
  coefficient.
4 a $\sum d^2 = 10$, $r_s = 0.714\dots$ limited evidence of positive
    correlation between the pairs of ranks
  b $\sum d^2 = 18$, $r_s = 0.8909\dots$ evidence of positive
    correlation between the pairs of ranks
  c $\sum d^2 = 158$, $r_s = -0.8809\dots$ evidence of negative
    correlation between the pairs of ranks
5 a 1   **b** –1   **c** 0.9   **d** 0.5
6 a $\sum d^2 = 48$
  b $r_s = 0.832\dots$. The more goals a team scores, the
    higher they are likely to be in the league table.
7 $\sum d^2 = 20$, $r_s = 0.762\dots$ The trainee vet is doing quite
  well as there is a fair degree of agreement between the
  trainee vet and the qualified vet. The trainee still has
  more to learn as r_s is less than 1.
8 a The marks are discrete rather than continuous
    values. The marks are not normally distributed.
  b $\sum d^2 = 28$, $r_s = 0.8303\dots$
    This shows a fairly strong positive correlation
    between the pairs of ranks of the marks awarded
    by the two judges so it appears they are judging the
    ice dances using similar criteria and with similar
    standards.
  c Give each of the equal values a rank equal to the
    mean of the tied ranks.
9 a The emphasis here is on ranks/marks so the data
    sets are unlikely to be from a bivariate normal
    distribution.
  b 0.580
  c Both show positive correlation but the judges agree
    more on the second dive.

Exercise 5B

1 a PMCC = –0.975 (3 s.f.)
  b Assume data are normally distributed. Critical
    values are ±0.8745. –0.975 < –0.8745 so reject H_0.
    There is evidence of correlation.
2 a $r = 0.677\dots$
  b Assume data are jointly normally distributed.
    H_0: $\rho = 0$; H_1: $\rho > 0$, 5% critical value is 0.5214.

Reject H_0. There is evidence to suggest that the
taller you are the older you are.
3 a H_0: $\rho_s = 0$; H_1: $\rho_s \neq 0$. Critical region is $r_s < -0.3624$
    and $r_s > 0.3624$
  b Reject H_0. There is reason to believe that engine
    size and fuel economy are related.
4 a H_0: $\rho = 0$, H_1: $\rho > 0$
    Critical value = 0.7887
    Since 0.774 is not in the critical region there is
    insufficient evidence of positive correlation.
  b $\sum d^2 = 10$
    $r_s = 1 - \dfrac{6 \times 10}{8 \times 63} = 0.881$ (3 s.f.)
  c e.g. The data are discrete results in a limited range.
    They are judgements, not measurements. It is also
    unlikely that these scores will both be normally
    distributed.
  d H_0: $\rho = 0$, H_1: $\rho > 0$
    Critical value: 0.8333
    Since 0.8333 is in the critical region there is
    evidence of positive correlation.
5 a Ranks are given rather than raw data.
  b $\sum d^2 = 46$
    $r_s = 1 - \dfrac{6 \times 46}{8 \times 63}$
    $r_s = 0.452$
  c H_0: $\rho_s = 0$; H_1: $\rho_s \neq 0$; critical values are ± 0.6249
    $0.452 < 0.6249$ or not significant or insufficient
    evidence to reject H_0. There is no evidence of
    agreement between the two judges.
6 $\sum d^2 = 76$, $r_s = -0.357$ (3 s.f.) H_0: $\rho_s = 0$; H_1 : $\rho_s < 0$.
  Critical value = –0.8929. There is no reason to reject
  H_0. There is insufficient evidence to show that a team
  that scores a lot of goals concedes very few goals.
7 a $\sum d^2 = 2$, $r_s = 0.943$
  b H_0: $\rho_s = 0$; H_1: $\rho_s > 0$. Critical value = 0.8286.
    Reject H_0. There is evidence that profits and takings
    are positively correlated.
8 a $\sum d^2 = 58$, $r_s = 0.797\dots$
  b H_0: $\rho_s = 0$; H_1: $\rho_s \neq 0$. Critical values = ±0.5874.
    Reject H_0: On this evidence it would seem that
    students who do well in Mathematics are likely to
    do well in Music.
9 Using Spearman's rank correlation coefficient:
  $\sum d^2 = 54$, $r_s = 0.6727\dots$
  H_0: $\rho_s = 0$; H_1: $\rho_s > 0$. Critical value 0.5636.
  Reject H_0: the child shows some ability in this task.
10 Using Spearman's rank correlation coefficient:
  $\sum d^2 = 64$, $r_s = -0.829$ (3 d.p.)
  H_0: $\rho_s = 0$; H_1: $\rho_s \neq 0$. Critical values = ±0.8857.
  Do not reject H_0: There is insufficient evidence of
  correlation between crop yield and wetness.
11 a PMCC since data is likely to be bivariate normal.
  b 2.5%   **c** 11

Chapter review 5

1 a $S_{jj} = 4413$, $S_{pp} = 5145$, $S_{jp} = 3972$
  b 0.834 (3 s.f.)
  c There is strong positive correlation, so Nimer is
    correct.
2 a Data is given in ranks rather than raw scores.
  b $r_s = 0.648$ (3 s.f.)
  c The null hypothesis is only rejected in favour
    of the alternative hypothesis if by doing so the
    probability of being wrong is less than or equal to
    the significance level.

d $H_0: \rho_s = 0$; $H_1: \rho_s > 0$. Critical value at 5% is 0.5636, so reject H_0. There is evidence of agreement between the two judges.

3 a Data given in rank/place order. The populations are not jointly normal. The relationship between data sets is non-linear.

b $\sum d^2 = 28$, $r_s = 0.766\ldots$

$H_0: \rho = 0$, $H_1: \rho > 0$, 2.5% critical value = 0.700

Reject H_0. There is evidence of agreement between the tutors at the 2.5% significance level. At the 1% significance level the test statistic and critical value are very close so it is inconclusive at this level of significance.

4 a $\sum d^2 = 56$, $r_s = 0.66$

b $H_0: \rho_s = 0$, $H_1: \rho_s > 0$, critical value = 0.5636
Reject H_0. There is a degree of agreement between the jumps.

5 Ranking so use Spearman's, $r_s = 0.714$. $H_0: \rho_s = 0$, $H_1: \rho_s > 0$. Critical value for 0.025 level = 0.7857. Do not reject H_0. There is insufficient evidence that the expert can judge relative age accurately.

6 a PMCC = 0.375 (3 s.f.)

b $H_0: \rho = 0$; $H_1: \rho > 0$. Critical value = 0.3783. Do not reject H_0. There is insufficient evidence of positive correlation between distance and time.

c Both distance and time are normally distributed.

7 a $\sum d^2 = 36$, $r_s = 0.5714\ldots$

b $H_0: \rho = 0$, $H_1: \rho \neq 0$, critical values = ± 0.7381
No reason to reject H_0. Students who do well in Geography do not necessarily do well in Statistics.

8 a 0.7857 (4 d.p.)

b Critical values = ± 0.7381
Reject H_0. There is evidence to suggest correlation between life expectancy and literacy.

c Only interested in order or cannot assume normality.

d i No change
ii Would increase since $d = 0$ and n is bigger.

9 a $r_s = 0.314$ (3 s.f.)

b $H_0: \rho_s = 0$; $H_1: \rho_s > 0$. Critical value = 0.8286. Do not reject H_0. There is insufficient evidence of agreement between the rankings of the judge and the vet.

10 a $S_{xx} = 1038.1$, $S_{yy} = 340.4$, $S_{xy} = 202.2$, $r = 0.340$ (3 d.p.)

b One or both given in rank order.
Population is not normal.
Relationship between data sets non-linear.

c $\sum d^2 = 112$, $r_s = 0.321$ (3 d.p.)

d $H_0: \rho_s = 0$, $H_1: \rho_s \neq 0$, critical value = ± 0.6485
Do not reject H_0. There is insufficient evidence of correlation.

11 a $S_{xx} = 6908.1$, $S_{yy} = 50\,288.1$, $S_{xy} = 17\,462$, $r = 0.937$ (3 d.p.)

b $\sum d^2 = 4$, $r_s = 0.976$ (3 d.p.)

c $H_0: \rho_s = 0$, $H_1: \rho_s \neq 0$, critical values = ± 0.6485
Reject H_0. For this machine there is insufficient evidence of correlation between age and maintenance costs.

12 a PMCC = -0.975 (3 s.f.)

b $H_0: \rho = 0$, $H_1: \rho < 0$, critical value = -0.5822, reject H_0. The greater the altitude the lower the temperature

c $H_0: \rho_s = 0$ (no association between hours of sunshine and temperature); $H_1: \rho_s \neq 0$, critical value = ± 0.7000
$0.767 > 0.7000$ so reject H_0. There is evidence of a positive association between hours of sunshine and temperature.

13 a You use a rank correlation coefficient if at least one of the sets of data isn't from a normal distribution, or if at least one of the sets of data is already ranked. It is also used if there is a non-linear association between the two data sets.

b $\sum d^2 = 78$, $r_s = 0.527\ldots$

c $H_0: \rho_s = 0$; $H_1: \rho_s > 0$. Critical value = 0.5636. Do not reject H_0. There is insufficient evidence of agreement between the qualified judge and the trainee judge.

14 $\sum d^2 = 120$, $r_s = 0.4285\ldots$

There is only a small degree of positive correlation between league position and home attendance.

15 a $H_0: \rho = 0$; $H_1: \rho > 0$. Critical value 0.5822. $0.972 > 0.5822$. Evidence to reject H_0. Age and weight are positively associated.

b $\sum d^2 = 26$, $r_s = 1 - \dfrac{6 \times 26}{9 \times 80} = 0.783$ (3 s.f.)

c Critical value = 0.6000
$0.783 > 0.600$ is evidence that actual weight and the boy's guesses are associated.

Challenge

a Since there are no ties, both the x's and the y's consist of the integers from 1 to n.

$$\sum x_i^2 = \sum y_i^2 = \sum_{r=1}^{n} r^2 = \frac{n(n+1)(2n+1)}{6}$$

b Since there are no ties, the x_i's and y_i's both consist of the integers from 1 to n. Hence $\sqrt{\sum(x_i - \bar{x})^2 \sum(y_i - \bar{y})^2}$

$$= \sqrt{\sum(x_i - \bar{x})^4} = \sum(x_i - \bar{x})^2$$

$$\bar{x} = \frac{\sum x_i}{n} = \frac{\frac{n(n+1)}{2}}{n} = \frac{n+1}{2}$$

$$\sum(x_i - \bar{x})^2 = \sum(x_i^2 - 2x_i\bar{x} + \bar{x}^2)$$

$$= \sum x_i^2 - 2\bar{x}\sum x_i + n\bar{x}^2$$

$$= \frac{n(n+1)(2n+1)}{6} - 2\left(\frac{n(n+1)}{2}\right)\left(\frac{n+1}{2}\right) + n\left(\frac{n+1}{2}\right)^2$$

$$= \frac{n(n+1)(2n+1)}{6} - n\left(\frac{n+1}{2}\right)^2$$

$$= n(n+1)\left(\frac{2n+1}{6} - \frac{n+1}{4}\right)$$

$$= \frac{n(n+1)(4n+2-3n-3)}{12}$$

$$= \frac{n(n+1)(n-1)}{12} = \frac{n(n^2-1)}{12}$$

c $\sum d_i^2 = \sum(y_i - x_i)^2$

$$= \sum x_i^2 - 2\sum x_i y_i + \sum y_i^2$$

$$= 2\sum x_i^2 - 2\sum x_i y_i$$

$$\Rightarrow \sum x_i y_i = \sum x_i^2 - \frac{\sum d_i^2}{2}$$

d $\sum(x_i - \bar{x})(y_i - \bar{y}) = \sum x_i(y_i - \bar{y}) - \sum \bar{x}(y_i - \bar{y})$

$= \sum x_i y_i - \bar{y} \sum x_i - \bar{x} \sum y_i + n\bar{x}\bar{y}$

$= \sum x_i y_i - n\bar{x}\bar{x} - n\bar{x}\bar{x} + n\bar{x}\bar{x}$

$= \sum x_i y_i - n\bar{x}\bar{x}$

$= \sum x_i^2 - \dfrac{\sum d_i^2}{2} - nx\bar{x}$

$= \dfrac{n(n+1)(2n+1)}{6} - \dfrac{n(n+1)(n+1)}{4} - \dfrac{\sum d_i^2}{2}$

$= \dfrac{n(n+1)(4n+2-3n-3)}{12} - \dfrac{\sum d_i^2}{2}$

$= \dfrac{n(n+1)(n-1)}{12} - \dfrac{\sum d_i^2}{2}$

$= \dfrac{n(n^2-1)}{12} - \dfrac{\sum d_i^2}{2}$

e From parts **b** and **d**

$\dfrac{\sum(x_i-\bar{x})(y_i-\bar{y})}{\sqrt{\sum(x_i-\bar{x})^2 \sum(y_i-\bar{y})^2}} = \dfrac{\dfrac{n(n^2-1)}{12} - \dfrac{\sum d_i^2}{2}}{\dfrac{n(n^2-1)}{12}}$

$= \dfrac{\dfrac{n(n^2-1)}{12}}{\dfrac{n(n^2-1)}{12}} - \dfrac{\dfrac{\sum d_i^2}{2}}{\dfrac{n(n^2-1)}{12}}$

$= 1 - \dfrac{6\sum d_i^2}{n(n^2-1)}$

CHAPTER 6

Prior knowledge check

1 0.4043

2 0.132

3 $H_0: p = 0.6$, $H_1: p \neq 0.6$
Here n is large and p is near 0.5 so a normal approximation can be used.
$B(100, 0.6) \approx N(60, 24)$

$P(X \geq 70) = P(W > 69.5) = P\left(Z > \dfrac{69.5 - 60}{\sqrt{24}}\right)$

$\qquad\qquad\qquad\qquad = P(Z > 1.94) = 0.026$

$0.025 > 0.025$, therefore we fail to reject H_0.
There is no evidence that David is wrong.

Exercise 6A

1 H_0: There is no difference between the observed and expected distributions.
H_1: There is a difference between the observed and expected distributions.

2 **a** H_0: The observed distribution is the same as the discrete uniform distribution.
H_1: The observed distribution is not the discrete uniform distribution.
b $X^2 = 1.6$

3 **a** H_0: There is no difference between the observed distribution and the discrete uniform distribution.
H_1: There is a difference between the observed distribution and the discrete uniform distribution.
b 150 **c** $X^2 = 14.33$

4 **a**

Mutation present	Yes	No
Expected frequency	120	40

b H_0: There is no difference between the observed and expected distributions.

H_1: There is a difference between the observed and expected distributions.
c $X^2 = 0.3$

5 **a**

Result	H	T
Expected frequency for fair coin	25	25
Expected frequency for biased coin	30	20

b $X^2_{\text{fair}} = 0.72$, $X^2_{\text{bias}} = 0.33$
c Since a lower goodness of fit score is better, it is more likely Jamal was flipping the biased coin.

6 Goodness of fit for Welsh men: 2.074, goodness of fit for Welsh women: 4.076. Therefore the distribution for English adults is a closer match for Welsh men than women.

Exercise 6B

1 6 degrees of freedom (7 observations, 1 constraint)

2 11.070

3 **a** 11.070 **b** 20.090 **c** 15.987

4 18.307

5 13.362

6 1.646

7 1.145

8 **a** 5.226 **b** 21.026

Exercise 6C

1 We calculate $X^2 = 4.33$. There are 5 degrees of freedom. $\chi^2_5 (5\%) = 11.070$, so there is insufficient evidence to reject the null hypothesis.

2 We expect 24 red and 96 gray. $X^2 = 4.21875$, whereas $\chi^2_1 (5\%) = 3.841$, so we reject the null hypothesis, the ratio is incorrect.

3 $X^2 = 8.05$, whereas $\chi^2_2 (2.5\%) = 7.378$, so we reject the null hypothesis, the expected distribution does not fit the data.

4 **a** Group together observations for '4 cats', '5 cats' and '>5 cats', so that the expected frequency exceeds 5. There are then 5 observations, and 1 constraint, so 4 degrees of freedom.
b $X^2 = 12.236$, whereas $\chi^2_4 (5\%) = 9.488$. Therefore we reject the null hypothesis, expected distribution doesn't fit data.

5 $X^2 = 737.6$, whereas $\chi^2_5 (5\%) = 11.071$, so we reject the null hypothesis that the distribution from 2000 is a good model for the data from 2015.

Exercise 6D

1 **a** H_0: the data may be modelled by Po(2).
$\chi^2_5(5\%) = 11\,070$,
$X^2 = 4.10$
No reason to reject H_0.
b Reduction by 1

2 Expected values 17, H_0: deliveries are uniformly distributed.
$\chi^2_5 (5\%) = 11.070$, $X^2 = 5.765$
No reason to reject H_0,

3 **a** 1.4
b $\chi^2_2 (10\%) = 4.605$, $X^2 = 5.04$
Reject H_0.
These data do not come from a Poisson distribution with $\lambda = 1.4$.

4 **a** 0.4
b $\chi^2_4 (5\%) = 5.991$, $X^2 = 3.19$
No reason to reject H_0

5 Expected values: 21.6, 16.2, 27, 5.4, 10.8
$\chi_4^2 (5\%) = 9.488$, $X^2 = 1.84$
No reason to reject H_0.
The number of accidents might well be constant at each factory.

6 $\lambda = 3.45$, $\chi_4^2(5\%) = 9.488$, $X^2 = 0.990$
No reason to reject H_0.
There is not sufficient evidence to suggest the data are not modelled by Po(3.45).

7 a Breakdowns are independent of each other, occur singly at random and at a constant rate.
  b $\lambda = 0.95$, H_0: the data can be modelled by Po(0.95)
   Expected values; 38.67, 36.74, 17.45, 7.14
   $\chi_2^2 (5\%) = 5.991$, $X^2 = 16.04$.
   Reject H_0. The breakdowns are not modelled by Po(0.95).

8 a $R = 43.75$ $S = 54.69$ $T = 43.75$
  b H_0: A binomial model is a suitable model
   H_1: A binomial model is not a suitable model
   $\chi^2 <$ c.v. so accept H_0.
   Conclude no reason to doubt data are from B(8, 0.5).
  c Mean would have to be calculated, an extra restriction.
   c.v. would be $\chi_5^2 (5\%) = 11.070$.
   $\chi^2 <$ c.v. so no change in conclusion.

9 a Unbiased estimator of variance = 2.4
  b Mean is close to variance.
  c $s = 27.2$ $t = 78.4$
  d H_0: the data are from Po(2.4)
   H_1: the data aren't from Po(2.4)
  e 3.5
  f This expected frequency of 3.5 < 5 so must be combined with E(X = 6) to give class '6 or more goals' which now has expected frequency 7.2 + 3.5 = 10.7
   We now have 7 classes after pooling and 2 restrictions so degrees of freedom = 7 – 2 = 5
  g $\chi^2 = 15.7$ c.v. = 11.070
   $\chi^2 >$ c.v. so reject H_0.
   Conclude there is evidence that the data can not be modelled by Po(2.4).

10 a $\frac{383}{148} = 2.59$ (2 d.p.)
  b It is assumed that plants occur at a constant average rate and occur independently and at random in the field.
  c $s = 37.24$ (2 d.p.) $t = 2.50$ (2 d.p.)
  d $x^2 <$ c.v. so accept H_0.
   Conclude there is no reason to doubt the data can be modelled by Po(2.59).

Exercise 6E

1 $x_2^2(5\%) = 5.991$, $x^2 = 0.899$
No reason to reject H_0.
No reason to believe N(3.8, 0.5²) is not a suitable model.

2 $x_2^2(5\%) = 5.991$, $x^2 = 0.0381$
No reason to reject H_0. N(58, 42) might well be a suitable model.

3 $x_2^2(5\%) = 5.991$, $x^2 = 3.20$
No reason to reject H_0. No evidence to suggest N(8, 0.92) is not a suitable model.

4 a $x_2^2(1\%) = 9.210$, $x^2 = 4.79$, $\mu = 23.4$, $\sigma = 10.222$
   Do not reject H_0.
   The data could come from a N(23.4, 10.2222) distribution.

b Shopkeeper could use this to help with stock control.

5 a $x_2^2(2.5\%) = 12.833$, $x^2 = 44.4$ Reject H_0
  b $\mu = 1.3165$, $\sigma = 0.0569$, $x_2^2(2.5\%) = 12.833$
   $x^2 = 5.78$ to 5.85 Accept H_0
  c The outfitter should use the model in **b** because it is based on the experimental evidence.
   The outfitter should order:
   size 1: 168   size 2: 417   size 3: 433   size 4: 182

6 $\chi_5^2 (0.05) = 11.070$, $X^2 = 12.36$ Reject H_0

Exercise 6F

1 $\nu = 2$, $\chi_2^2 (5\%) = 5.991$

2 H_0: Ownership is not related to city
H_1: Ownership is related to city
$\chi_2^2 (5\%) = 5.991$, $X^2 = 13.1$
Reject H_0.

3 a $(3 - 1)(3 - 1) = 4$
  b $\chi_4^2 (5\%) = 9.488$
   Reject H_0. There is an association between groups and grades.

4 H_0: There is no relationship between results
$\chi_4^2 (5\%) = 9.488$, $X^2 = 8.56$
Do not reject H_0. There is no reason to believe there is a relationship between results

5 $\chi_2^2 (5\%) = 5.991$, $X^2 = 1.757$
Do not reject H_0. There is no evidence to suggest association between station and lateness.

6 $\chi_4^2 (1\%) = 13.277$
Reject H_0. Gender and grade appear to be associated.

7 a

	Observed				Expected	
	A	**B**	**Total**		**A**	**B**
OK	47	28	75		45	30
Defective	13	12	25		15	10
Total	60	40	100		–	–

  b H_0: Factory and quality are not associated.
   H_1: Factory and quality are associated.
   $\chi_1^2 (0.05) = 3.841$
   $$\sum \frac{(O_i - E_i)^2}{E_i} = \frac{2^2}{45} + \frac{2^2}{30} + \frac{2^2}{15} + \frac{2^2}{10} = 0.8888$$
   $0.8888 < 3.841$
   Do not reject H_0. There is no evidence between factory involved and quality.

8 H_0: Gender and how easy it is to catch flu are not associated.
H_1: Gender and how easy it is to catch flu are associated.

Observed

	Boys	**Girls**	**Total**
Flu	15	8	23
No flu	7	20	27
Total	22	28	50

Expected

	Boys	**Girls**
	10.12	12.88
	11.88	15.12
	–	–

$\chi_1^2 (5\%) = 3.841$, $X^2 = 7.78$
Reject H_0. There is evidence for an association between gender and susceptibility to flu.

9 $\chi_2^2 (5\%) = 5.991$, $X^2 = 27.27$
Reject H_0. There is evidence of an association between the gender of an animal and the beach on which it is found.

10 H_0: There is no association between age and number of bank cards.

H_1: There is an association between age and number of bank cards.

$\chi_1^2 (5\%) = 3.841, X^2 = 8.31$

Reject H_0. There is an association between age and the number of bank cards possessed.

11 a H_0: There is no association between gym and whether or not a member got injured.

H_1: There is an association between gym and whether or not a member gets injured.

b $\dfrac{34}{865} \times 175 = 6.88$ (2 d.p.)

c Expected frequencies are:

Gym	A	B	C	D
Expected injured	9.32	10.14	6.88	7.66
Expected uninjured	227.68	247.86	168.12	187.34

from which we calculate $X^2 = 7.732$

There are 3 degrees of freedom and χ_3^2, so we do not reject the null hypothesis, there is not enough evidence at the 5% significance level to think that any gym is more dangerous than the others.

12 a H_0: There is no association between science studied and pay.

H_1: There is an association between science studied and pay.

b The expected frequencies are:

Science studied	Salary		
	£0–£40k	£40k–£60k	>£60k
Biology	70.19	26.40	7.41
Chemistry	72.89	27.42	7.69
Physics	74.92	28.18	7.90

from which we calculate $X^2 = 2.031$.

The number of degrees of freedom is $(3 - 1) \times (3 - 1) = 4$ and $\chi_4^2 (5\%) = 9.49$, therefore we do not reject the null hypothesis, there is not enough evidence to at the 5% significance level to think that the subject studied has an effect on pay.

Chapter review 6

1 23.209

2 15.507

3 $\nu = 8$, critical region $\chi^2 > 15.507$

4 $\nu = 6, 12.592$

5 H_0: Taking the medicine and catching a cold are independent (not associated)

H_1: Taking the medicine and catching a cold are not independent (associated)

$$\sum \frac{(O - E)^2}{E} = 2.53$$

$\nu = 1$ $\chi_1^2 (5\%) = 3.841 > 2.53$

No reason to believe that the chance of catching a cold is affected by taking the new the medicine.

6 H_0: Poisson distribution is a suitable model

H_1: Poisson distribution is not a suitable model

From these data $\lambda = \frac{52}{80} = 0.65$

Expected frequencies 41.76, 27.15, $\dfrac{8.82, 2.27}{11.09}$

$\alpha = 0.05, \nu = 3 - 1 - 1 = 1$; critical value = 3.841

$$\sum \frac{(O - E)^2}{E} = 1.312$$

Since 1.312 is not the critical region there is insufficient evidence to reject H_0 and we can conclude that the Poisson model is a suitable one.

7 27.5, 22.5; 27.5, 22.5

$$\sum \frac{(O - E)^2}{E} = \frac{(23 - 27.5)^2}{27.5} + \dots + \frac{(18 - 22.5)^2}{22.5} = 3.27$$

$\alpha = 0.10 \Rightarrow \chi^2 > 2.705$

$3.27 > 2.705$

Since 3.27 is in the critical region there is evidence of association between gender and test result.

8 a Each box has an equal chance of being opened – we would expect each box to be opened 20 times.

b $\chi_4^2 (5\%) = 9.488, \chi^2 = 2.3$

No reason to reject H_0, A discrete uniform distribution could be a good model.

9 a 0.72

b $\chi_2^2 (5\%) = 5.991, X^2 = 2.62$

No reason to reject H_0. The B(5, 0.72) could be a good model.

10 $\lambda = 0.654, \nu = 2, X^2 = 21.506$,

$\chi_2^2 (5\%) = 5.991$. Reject H_0.

Po(0.654) distribution is not a suitable model.

11 $\chi_2^2 (5\%) = 5.991, X^2 = 4.74\dots$

12 a 4.28

b $\chi_4^2 (5\%) = 9.488, X^2 = 1.18$

No reason to reject H_0. Po(4.28) could be a good model.

No reason to reject H_0. Po(4.28) could be a good model.

13 $\chi_1^2 (5\%) = 3.841. X^2 = 10.42$. Reject H_0.

There is evidence to suggest association between left-handedness and gender in this population.

14 a H_0: There is no association between gender and preferred subject.

H_1: There is an association between gender and preferred subject.

b $\dfrac{(28 + 40) \times (45 + 40 + 45)}{300} \approx 29.47$

c The expected frequencies are:

		Subject		
		Physics	Biology	Chemistry
Gender	**Male**	67.43	38.53	64.03
	Female	51.57	29.47	48.97

from which we calculate $X^2 = 8.685$.

d There are $(3 - 1) \times (2 - 1) = 2$ degrees of freedom, and $\chi_2^2 (1\%) = 9.21$. Therefore we do not reject the hypothesis.

e Since $\chi_2^2 (5\%) = 5.991$, we would reject the null hypothesis at the 5% significance level.

15 a **i** $P(X = 1) \approx 0.2504$

ii $P(X > 2) \approx 0.3639$

b $\sum k \times O_k = \frac{129}{60} = 2.15$

c $a = 16.15, b = 1.36$

d H_0: The data can be modelled by a Poisson distribution with mean 2.15.

H_1: The data cannot be modelled by a Poisson distribution with mean 2.15.

e The chi-squared test is not very effective if the expected values are below 5, so we combine expected values in order to make sure each of the expected values are at least 5.

f The test statistic is $X^2 = 2.507$. There are 3 degrees of freedom (5 observations, and 2 constraints since we estimated the mean from the data). From the tables we see $\chi^2_3 (5\%) = 7.815$. Therefore we do not reject the null hypothesis.

16 a Using the midpoints of each range, we calculate the mean and variance. Mean = 14.14, Var = 17.11

b We calculate expected frequencies as follows:

Length of call (l)	$l < 5$	$5 \leqslant l < 10$	$10 \leqslant l < 15$	$15 \leqslant l < 20$	$20 \leqslant l$
Expected frequency	6.78	72.44	211.95	169.68	39.14

The null and alternative hypotheses are:
H_0: The call length can be modelled by a normal distribution
H_1: The call length can't be modelled by a normal distribution
From this we can calculate $X^2 = 3.242$. There are 2 degrees of freedom, since there are 5 observations, we estimated 2 parameters, and we have the constraint of the total summing to 500. Thus the critical value is $\chi^2_2 (5\%) = 5.991$. Hence we do not reject the null hypothesis, the length of call can be modelled by a normal distribution.

Review exercise 2

1 a N(90, 0.25)
  Application of central limit theorem (as sample large)
  b 0.0228
2 0.4875
3 a 0.1
  b 0.5539
  c Accurate since n is large.
4 a 0.0699
  b 0.0810
  c 0.0787; values are close so the central limit theorem does provides a reasonable estimate.
5 0.2593
6 a 0.0443
  b 20
  c 0.3325
7 a $\frac{13}{21}$ or 0.619 (3 s.f.)
  b $H_0 : \rho = 0, H_1 : \rho > 0$
  5% critical value = 0.6429
  0.619 < 0.6429 so do not reject H_0. The evidence does not show positive correlation between the judges' marks, so the person's claim is justified.
8 a $r_s = -\frac{11}{15}$ or –0.733 (3 s.f.)
  b $H_0 : \rho = 0$; $H_1 : \rho < 0$
  5% critical value = –0.5636.
  –0.733 < –0.5636 so reject H_0. There is evidence of a significant negative correlation between the price of an ice cream and the distance from the pier. The further from the pier you travel, the less money you are likely to pay for an ice cream.
9 a The variables cannot be assumed to be normally distributed.
  b $r_s = \frac{5}{7}$ or 0.714 (3 s.f.)
  c $H_0 : \rho = 0$; $H_1 : \rho > 0$.
  5% critical value = 0.8286.
  0.714 < 0.8286 so do not reject H_0. There is no evidence that the relative vulnerabilities of the different age groups are similar for the two diseases.

10 a i

b i $r_s = \frac{23}{28}$ or 0.821 (3 s.f.)
  ii $H_0 : \rho = 0$; $H_1 : \rho > 0$.
  5% critical value = 0.7143.
  0.821 > 0.7143 so reject H_0. There is evidence of a (positive) correlation between the ranks awarded by the judges.

11 a

b The strength of the linear link between two variables.
c $S_{tt} = 26.589$; $S_{pp} = 152.444$; $S_{tp} = 59.524$
d 0.93494...
e $H_0 : \rho = 0$, $H_1 : \rho > 0$.
  5% critical value = 0.7155.
  0.935 > 0.7155 so reject H_0; reactant and product are positively correlated.
f Linear correlation is significant but the scatter diagram looks non-linear. The product moment correlation coefficient should not be used here since the association/relationship is not linear.
12 a $H_0 : \rho = 0$, $H_1 : \rho < 0$.
  5% critical value = –0.8929
  –0.93 < –0.8929 so reject null hypothesis. There is evidence supporting the geographer's claim.
  b i No effect since rank stays the same.
  ii It will increase since $d = 0$ and n is bigger.
  c The mean of the tied ranks is given to each and then the PMCC is used.
13 a $p = 0.1$
  b $r = 28.5$ (1 d.p.), $s = 100 - 91 = 9.0$ (1 d.p.)
  c t.s. > c.v. so reject H_0.
  (significant result) binomial distribution is not a suitable model
  d Defective items do not occur independently or not with constant probability.
14 a B(5, 0.5)
  b Insufficient evidence to reject H_0.
  B(5, 0.5) is a suitable model.
  No evidence that coins are biased.

15 a $p = \dfrac{223}{1000} = 0.223$

b $r = 10.74$, $s = 30.20$, $t = 3.28$

c H_0: $B(10, 0.2)$ is a suitable model for these data.
H_1: $B(10, 0.2)$ is not a suitable model for these data.

d Since $t < 5$, the last two groups are combined and $v = 5 - 1 = 4$. Since there are then 5 cells and the parameter p is given.

e $4.17 < 9.488$ so not significant or do not reject null hypothesis.
The binomial distribution with $p = 0.2$ is a suitable model for the number of cuttings that do not grow.

16 Critical value $\chi^2_3(5\%) = 5.991$. From Poisson 5.47 is not in the critical region so accept H_0. Number of computer failures per day can be modelled by a Poisson distribution.

17 a Reject H_0.
Conclude there is evidence of an association between Mathematics and English grades.

b May have some expected frequencies <5 (and hence need to pool rows/columns).

18 $3.841 > 2.59$. There is insufficient evidence to reject H_0. There is no association between a person's gender and their acceptance of the offer of a flu injection.

19 $14.19 > 9.210$ so significant result or reject null hypothesis.
There is evidence of an association between course taken and gender.

20 $3.47619 < 9.488$
There is no evidence of association between treatment and length of survival.

21 $2.4446 < 5.991$
so insufficient evidence to reject H_0.
No association between age and colour preference.

22 $3.2 < 15.1$ therefore no evidence to suggest it is not uniformly distributed

Challenge

a $r = 19.15$, $s = 19.15$

b $12.12 < 15.086$ so accept H_0.
The distribution can be modelled by a $N \sim (360, 20)$.

Exam practice

1 a Quota sampling is the most appropriate since we do not have a sampling frame to select the birds from.

b The number of birds from each type is:

Blackbird	Sparrow	Chaffinch	Woodpecker
160	80	80	40

Catch a bird. If the quota is not full, record it, tag it and release it. If a bird is caught which is already tagged, ignore it and release. Continue until all quota are full.

2 a H_0: $\rho_s = 0$
H_1: $\rho_s > 0$
$r_s = 1 - \dfrac{6 \times 34}{10(99)} = 0.794$
Critical value = 0.5636
Reject H_0
There is a positive correlation between the scores on the theory paper and the programming paper.

b Student I and Student E will now both have the same score and so will need to share their ranks as 2.5 each. You would then, because of the tied ranks, need to use the PMCC formula with the ranks.

3 H_0: A continuous uniform distribution ($X \sim U[0, 60]$) is a good model
H_1: A continuous uniform distribution ($X \sim U[0, 60]$) is not a good model
Do not reject H_0
A continuous uniform distribution ($X \sim U[0, 60]$) is a good model

4 a $E(D) = 5$

b $Var(D) = 181$

c $P(5X > 3Y) = 0.6443$

d $P(\bar{X} - X_3 < 1) = 0.7291$

5 H_0: there is no association between preference of chocolate and company
H_1: there is an association between preference of chocolate and company
$X^2 = 9.895$
$\chi^2_2(0.05) = 5.991$
Reject H_0:
There is an association between preference of chocolate and company.

6 Let $C \sim N(41.2, 3.6^2)$ with μ_c being the population mean for the children.
Let $A \sim N(47.6, 2.7^2)$ with μ_a being the population mean for the adults.
H_0: $\mu_a - \mu_c = 5$
H_1: $\mu_a - \mu_c > 5$
Test statistic = 2.098
Critical value = 1.96
Reject H_0
Children do complete the puzzle more than 5 seconds quicker than adults.

7 a $\bar{x} = 275.8$, $s^2 = 4.612$

b 275.2, 276.4

c Since we do not know the original distribution, the central limit theorem allows us to approximate the sample mean as a normal distribution so we can then find the confidence interval.

d The printed mass is completely below the confidence interval and so the printed mass is incorrect (based on this sample)

INDEX